Arthur Calder-Marsh[...]
attended Oxford in th[...]
of the generation w[...]
others, Evelyn Waugh [...]
Quennell. Novelist and [...], his most famous
works include *About Levy* and *The Scarlet Boy*.
Today, Arthur Calder-Marshall lives with his
wife in Twickenham.

Dear Michael —
This is for keeps.
This was one of my fathers.
first Novels — and I would love
you to have a copy.

Best wishes
Anna Calder-Marshall

ARTHUR CALDER-MARSHALL

The Magic of My Youth

CARDÍNAL

*To my Father and Mother
and the memory of my brother Bobby*

A Cardinal Book

First published in Great Britain by
Rupert Hart-Davis in 1951
Published in Cardinal by Sphere Books Ltd, 1990

Reproduced, printed and bound in Great Britain by
Cox & Wyman Ltd, Reading

ISBN 0 7474 0625 1

Sphere Books Ltd
A Division of
Macdonald & Co (Publishers) Ltd
Orbit House
1 New Fetter Lane
London EC4A 1AR
A member of Maxwell Macmillan Pergamon Publishing Corporation

CONTENTS

★

FOREWORD

*

I NEVER intended to write this book. One day I began to make notes in an exercise book; and because it
suddenly returned to my mind, I wrote down the story
of Driberg and The Beast, which Driberg had told me
just after Crowley's death. But as I wrote, I found that
by a natural association of ideas one memory began to
flow into another, all of them linked in one way or another with the interest in The Beast or ritual magic which
was the last refuge of my adolescence. It was a pleasant
change from the work I had been doing, to try at a distance of between twenty and twenty-five years to perceive what had really been happening at a time when I was
too engrossed in myself to be particularly interested in
other people. Rupert Hart-Davis and David Garnett, to
whom I showed the early chapters, gave me the en-
couragement and assistance to continue uninterruptedly
with the work, and this book is the result.

The ways in which it is not true will be immediately
apparent. Lengthy conversations are not remembered
verbatim over a quarter of a century. The more accurate
a description appears the less likely it is to correspond
faithfully with the vision of a place or person at the time.
Memory and conjecture rather than research have been
my guides.

In Chapter Five, I am indebted to Mr Richard Hughes
for his recollections of Raoul Loveday at Oxford and to
Miss Betty May for the description in *Tiger Woman* of

her married life with Loveday and the events at Cefalu; though the interpretation is throughout my own. My thanks are due to Messrs Duckworth, the publishers of *Tiger Woman*, and my apologies to Miss Betty May for not obtaining her personal permission to consult her narrative. That her permission was not obtained was not due to lack of trying. Diligent enquiry among her old friends yielded no clue to her whereabouts.

I am indebted to Miss Nina Hamnett and the Librarian of *Reynolds News* for verification of the details of the Ione de Forrest case in Chapter Seven.

Apart from this, the book is the product not of research but recollection, and the truth at which it aims is truth to memory.

Memory however is of many kinds, and the type of memory on which I have drawn varies from chapter to chapter, in certain cases even from paragraph to paragraph. In The See-er, for example, the life-story of Auntie Helen was clearer to me twenty years ago than it is today; its re-telling is a matter purely of recollection. On the other hand, The Poet 'At Home' is an extreme example of the opposite process, of 'remembering up.' In writing it I tried to think of what 'must have happened;' and when new details occurred to me, I admitted them on the grounds that if they did not happen that way, at any rate they should have done. My father, from whom I inherit this lucky or unfortunate quality of 'creative memory,' assures me that in fact the visit took place in the afternoon and he said 'almost nothing, sitting there feeling bored and very uncomfortable.' That I have, with his indulgence, allowed the chapter to stand as I remembered it, will give the reader some idea of the latitude which I have allowed myself.

One of the great difficulties of trying at the age of forty-two to retell the events of adolescence is to decide at what age to make one's judgements, whether to mellow the brashness of youth with the tolerance and compassion of middle age or to leave it naked and callow. I have tried as far as possible to present the 'I' character as the gawky observer that he was at the time, and to keep my present opinion in the background. But there are certain times when the forty-two-year-old finds interpretations which were not apparent at the time. Though, for example, I was aware at the end of my time at Oxford of the reason for Vickybird's rustication, I did not realise till I came to write this book that the same reason lay behind his flight into anonymity.

In brief, I have adopted the principles which William Hazlitt enunciated in his introduction to the serial publication of his *Conversations of James Northcote, R.A.*:

I have feigned whatever I have pleased. I have forgotten, mistaken, mis-stated, altered, transposed a number of things. All that can be relied upon for certain is a striking anecdote or a sterling remark or two in each page. These belong as a matter of right to my principal speaker. . . . I have, however, generally taken him as my lay-figure or model, and worked upon it, *selon mon gré*, by fancying how he would express himself. . . . I have also introduced little incidental details that never happened ; thus, by lying, giving a greater air of truth to the scene—an art understood by most historians! In a word, Mr Northcote is only answerable for the wit, sense and spirit there may be in these papers; I take all the dullness, impertinence, and malice upon myself.

A. C-M.

London, July 1951.

Part One

THE POET AND THE SEE-ER

Prelude

The Illusionist of Islington

*

ON the evening of the day when the death was announced of Aleister Crowley, the self-styled Knight Elect of the Sangrail, Master of Thelema and τo Μεγαθηρίον The Beast 666 of the Apocalypse, Tom Driberg was dining at a house in Kensington.

Over dinner Driberg related how, when he was writing the William Hickey column in the *Daily Express*, he received one day a telephone call from a man who asked him if he would be interested in acquiring any Crowleyana. On replying that he might be, Tom was told that he should call at an address in one of the less fashionable streets of Islington at six p.m. on the following day.

There he found a man who said that though, as a theatrical conjuror by profession, he usually had no difficulty in gaining his livelihood, at that present moment, owing to ill health and bad fortune, he was in straitened circumstances. This was the only reason which would induce him to part with the rare and curious works of the Master.

Crowley's literary work was in fact curious only by reason of its dullness, if exception be made of the pornographic novel which he wrote for one of his wives who complained that she had nothing to read. The only thing

15

Driberg picked out as interesting was a red leather volume enclosed in a beautiful eighteenth-century silver holder designed originally for a Book of Hours. This volume, which had been made especially to fit the silver holder, was one of Crowley's private diaries, in which he was used to record his sexual and magical operations. It contained the names of a surprising number of people whom one would not have connected either with magic in general or Crowley's brand in particular, and their signed oaths of allegiance to The Beast.

Driberg asked the conjuror how this volume had come into his possession; but this the man was unwilling or unable to disclose.

Some time later Crowley gave dinner to Driberg. It was an excellent dinner, as anyone who ate with The Beast would know. For when he had money, there was no one more generous—there is no host like the man who has just borrowed a tenner—and when he had no money, he thought nothing of playing host with the menu and wine-list and passing the bill to his guest.

At the end of dinner Crowley ordered a bottle of Perrier-Jouet '21, and later drew a magic symbol on the back of the menu and passed it to Driberg, asking him to describe what he saw in it; a clairvoyant parlour game of which he was fond and which he practised himself before coming to any important decision.

Driberg stared at it for some time and then slowly began to describe the red leather volume obscured by a silver monstrance with A on its left hand, Ω on its right hand and beneath it IHS.

Crowley leaned forward in a state of violent excitement. "What's inside?" he said. "Open it, man. Tell me what you can read."

Driberg waved him on one side and then tried once more to concentrate. "It's no good," he said at last; "you shouldn't have interrupted." He looked at his watch and got up rapidly. "I'd no idea it was so late. I've got to dash to Fleet Street. But," he added, patting The Beast on the shoulder as he left, "perhaps if you gave me another bottle of Perrier-Jouet '21 as excellent as this sometime, I might be able to tell you what was inside."

Telling this story that evening in Kensington, Driberg was annoyed because he couldn't remember the name of the conjuror in Islington, and he felt that without it his story was implausible and unauthentic. It worried him for the rest of the evening; the name was there, round a corner in his memory, but it wouldn't appear. Even when he left, some time after midnight, he was still stalking it through the back of his mind.

The last trains and buses had gone, and as the evening was wet and rather misty, the chances of catching a homing cab were small. He pulled up his coat collar and set off to walk home.

He was going up Kensington Church Street, when out of the darkness of a shop entrance there stepped a young man, who asked him for a light. There was nothing remarkable about him, except that he was sheltering in a shop entrance at that hour without a hat, a mackintosh or overcoat.

"Aren't you going home?" Tom asked.

"I meant to stay in this evening," the young man said. "I read in my room until nine o'clock. Then I started to

17

undress, to go to bed. And suddenly, I don't know why, I felt I had to be with people. I put my clothes on and went out, but instead of going to my local, I hopped on a bus and came down here." He pointed to a pub. "I went in there; never been there before, and I drank and talked till closing time. And then they turned us out and gradually all the people went home and the lights went out in the pub and I thought, 'You planned to have an early night.' But I just couldn't go back to my room, I don't know why? Funny, isn't it?"

Driberg pocketed his matches, agreed that it was funny and began to walk up the hill towards Notting Hill Gate. He had gone a dozen paces, when from behind him came the voice of the young man, calling through the drizzle, "I say, have you seen Cosmo lately?"

Cosmo was the name which had eluded him the whole evening. COSMO THE GREAT, ILLUSIONIST. Driberg wheeled round and shouted to the young man, who was still standing in the rain under the street lamp, "Do *you* know Cosmo?"

"Me?" called the young man in a surprised voice. "No!"

Then he turned and strode rapidly away in the direction of the Church of St Mary Abbots.

If this was, as Driberg at that moment may have felt, the last appearance of the Knight Elect of the Sangrail before his departure to the Inferno, it was in character. He operated, many confirm, by laws of coincidence. Once you heard his name you heard it everywhere.

Or was it that your ears were alert for his mention and

that the presence in London of a Gnostic black magician was subject for more comment in the twentieth century than a meeting of the World Churches in the Central Hall, Westminster? The Beast himself would plump for the supernatural explanation, however absurd it might be. Myself, I hazard no guess. All I know is that, having spent the first fifteen years of my life in ignorance of Crowley's existence, I became aware of him from four separate sources in the course of six months: from a Sunday newspaper, from my brother at Oxford, from a vision of the Tiger Woman, Betty May, in full Bacchanal at a Bloomsbury Hotel and, most remarkable of all, from the Steyning Poet.

Chapter One

The Poet

★

IF you are to appreciate the singularity of the Poet, you must first know something of Steyning in the 1920's. My grandfather had moved there at the turn of the century, on retirement from his profession of chartered accountant. His children were grown up. He had married for the second time and he was attracted by the peace of this inaccessible market town, which was reached only by trains running from Horsham to Shoreham, one of the slowest branch lines on the London, Brighton and South Coast Railway's network. It was reputed that just as farmers put aged carthorses out to grass rather than consign them to the knacker's yard, the railway company retired ageing locomotives, which in a more competitive age might have found their way immediately to the scrapheap, to the Shoreham and Horsham line, drawing superannuated coaches. backwards and forwards.

Steyning exactly suited my grandfather's needs, and he had built for himself a red-brick house in a new road, looking over a marshy valley to the ruined walls of Bramber Castle, below which twice or three times a day senile puff-puffs would trundle antique coaches, the moribund leading the moribund like the bath-chair attendants on Eastbourne front. He became the Brigadier of the local

Church Lads' Brigade and the superintendent of the Sunday School.

I should like to have served under him in the Church Lads' Brigade, because his method of teaching was original. Instead of re-telling the old Bible stories, as so many of his less imaginative colleagues did, he wrote special short stories based upon incidents in the life of Steyning. Steyning lies between the villages of Bramber to the south and of Henfield to the north, a fact which inspired my grandfather to create his own village of Bramfield, where life bore great similarity to life in Steyning, except that moral laws had an inexorable logic which was blurred in real life. When, for example, the Steyning blacksmith got tight at Christmas, he came before the Magistrates' bench and was fined five shillings. When, on the following Sunday, the blacksmith of Bramfield committed the same offence, it became plain that this lapse was not an isolated offence, but one link in a chain of moral degradation that led to the loss of the blacksmith's home, his wife's death through tuberculosis, his own violent demise in a tavern brawl and his summary despatch to Hell. His unhappy children, however, were saved because they all belonged to the Church Lads' Brigade or the Sunday School and thus succeeded in getting jobs, according to their sex, as kitchenmaids and gardeners' boys in the employment either of the vicar himself or of a kindly old gentleman who was the Sunday School superintendent.

There is no doubt that my grandfather considered that he had taken his place in that quiet village community. But to the natives of Steyning, he and the other old people like him who had retired to Steyning were pioneers of the hordes of Londoners who later in the century came to destroy the quiet beauty which they believed they sought.

My grandfather expressed his emotions towards the village of his adoption in a poem called *A Reverie at Steyning*, which he printed at his own expense and retailed through the local stationer for the modest sum of threepence, all proceeds to be donated to the Church Lads' Brigade. It began briskly with the quatrain:

> I see the roofs of dear old Steyning,
> Quaint old-fashioned market town.
> Some are roofed with Sussex limestone,
> Some are red; and some are brown.

It was not until twenty years later that I went to live in Steyning. My grandfather had moved by then to the churchyard. His Church Lads' Brigade insignia were relegated to a loft, in a cardboard box together with four mothballs and his truss. But dear old Steyning was still a quaint old-fashioned market town with sheep and cattle clattering down the street on market days, with the same shops and most of the same shopkeepers as my grandfather had first known.

There were perhaps a couple of dozen more retired cooks letting lodgings during the summer. But the train service was so bad that Steyning had escaped the development that was ruining the Home Counties all along the main lines.

Distinctions of class were well-defined. There were the ' local people,' who washed, sewed, scrubbed, dug, cooked and catered for the gentry, most of whom were elderly retired people. And there were the local professional people, the vicar, the headmaster of the grammar school,

the doctors, the solicitors, the stationmaster, the auction-
eer, the builder. The social position of everybody was
clearly marked.

The only person who fitted into no social category was
the Poet. He lived in what was regarded then as a tumble-
down cottage but which today would probably fetch
seven thousand pounds as a superb example of Tudor
black and white. Swinging from a bracket set in the wall
hung a sign announcing the Vine Press. The wall itself
was almost hidden in summer by the leaves of an ancient
and infertile vine, and in a window of the room below the
sign stood a large, dusty hand-press.

If the people of Steyning, looking through this window, had ever seen the Poet or his devils working at this
press, they would have found it easier to place him in a
social pigeon-hole. But this never happened. Each morning he would emerge from Vine Cottage with a string bag
and an obese white bitch and make for the High Street.

He carried an ash stick, and he was always dressed in a
Norfolk jacket and knickerbockers, with stockings which
rode in rucks around his spindly legs, and shoes so old
that the leather was cracked.

He had thin venous hands and a head which, by nature
disproportionately large for his body, was magnified by
dark Medusa locks which rose from his scalp and tumbled
curling down his forehead.

To judge from a painting of him in youth, he had been
handsome beyond the ordinary. But he had later contracted an eczema which disfigured his nose, and a malady
of the spirit which plagued his whole life. On the care of
his teeth he was scrupulous. He brushed them after every

meal, even taking his toothbrush with him if invited out to lunch. But in his person he had lost all vanity or self-respect. Smudges would remain on his face for hours, sometimes even days. He shaved customarily every third day, and it was hard to know which was the more distressing, his tramp-like half-beard or his face clean-shaven. For he never mastered the skill of shaving, and when he had done with hacking at his hairs, his face was as scarred and gashed as if he had been dragged through a thicket of brambles.

To his clothes he paid as little attention as to his person. Though this was a time for plus-fours and beltless sports-coats, the people of Steyning would have accepted the knickerbockers and Norfolk jacket, if he or his wife had made some attempt to patch them up. But of the holes at his elbows and knees, the frayed ends of his sleeves, the Poet seemed oblivious, or, what perhaps was even worse, almost proud.

This was the supreme outrage. The gentry would have accepted a starving poet, living for his art, if only he had washed. They would have pardoned his dirt and tatters, if only he had seemed ashamed of them. But the air of arrogance was more than they could bear.

As he walked along the street with his stick over his arm and the string bag in his hand, he looked like a king in motley or Charlie Chaplin playing Haroun al Raschid. While the bitch alternately sniffed at the surfaces popular in canine society and made its own contributions to The Dog's World, that archetype of the wall newspaper, he would saunter along singing to himself, "The first time I met her she was dressed all in red" or *Johnny Hall*, that threnody of the unitesticular, which he had found so popular during his wartime service in the P.B.I.

In the middle of a verse he would turn round to discover that the bitch had wandered into a lumber-yard on one of those social calls which engross so much of dog-owners' lives. For a minute or two he would call her to heel in a peremptory treble and then, accepting the fact that the bitch would come in her own good time, he would turn to an adenoidal child, sucking its pinafore in a cottage doorway, while from its nose descended a catarrhal pearl. "Ah, there's my ducky diamonds, my little princess," he would say, fumbling in his pocket for a shining halfpenny. "Lo, here is a golden guinea! Go thou and buy a lollipop."

The gentry of Steyning were careful people, subscribing to acknowledged charities the minimum consistent with their own estimate of their social position. They disapproved on principle of distributing indiscriminate largesse which paid no social dividends, and they strongly resented it when this was done by a shabby little man, without a penny to his name, who furthermore attended neither church nor chapel and subscribed nothing to the Bellringers. Everybody agreed that he whispered to the child, "Now remember, there is no God!" and the vicar's wife maintained that he added, "And tell your Daddy to vote Labour at the next election."

Even to his friends, who knew him not as the Poet but as Vickybird, he could be a disconcerting companion. He had a loud and uncontagious laugh, as abrupt to begin and end as the cry of a parrokeet. Walking with him in a public street, I used to try to avoid anything even remotely mirth-making, because I was so embarrassed by his strident cackle. But his humour was so intricately wired that even the most circumspect conversation might set it off, clanging through the quaint old-fashioned market town, like those burglar alarms which in London are frequently to be heard outside foreign fur-shops.

To friend, foe or complete stranger his manners were polite to the point of parody. See him, for example, in the Post Office, buying a penny stamp. At this moment the vicar's wife, a worthy woman with a sincere conviction that Vickybird is the anti-Christ, makes for the door. Vickybird leaps to anticipate her, and as he holds the door open for her to pass, he bows solemnly from the waist, with the palm of his hand placed on his stomach. "The top of this wondrous morning to you, fayre ladye!" he exclaims.

At this moment his walking-stick falls off his arm and clatters to the floor. He bends down smartly to prevent it tripping her up. The door catches him from behind and his head strikes the vicar's wife in the pit of the stomach. He straightens up to apologise and knocks her shopping-bag to the ground. Carrots, butter, sausages and onions strew the floor and as Vickybird runs to collect those which have rolled the furthest, the dog sniffs at those he has retrieved.

A casual courtesy, but Puck with his deliberate malice could not create chaos quicker than Vickybird by a single act of unsolicited helpfulness. Little wonder then that those who disliked him believed that his attentions were malevolent.

Though he was so careless in his person and oblivious to the untidiness of his home, he was the neatest of men out of doors. He hated litter in the street or in the country. As a dog will dart off after any distracting scent, Vickybird even in the middle of conversation would swoop down and pick up a dirty piece of paper, a matchbox and even on occasion a spent match and poke it down a drain or bury it from sight. In doing so, he was unconscious of his surroundings, sometimes swooping like a hungry gull to rescue a piece of tinfoil from a stranger's feet. He collected tinfoil and made it into heavy balls, which he presented to hospitals.

People whose motives were carefully calculated believed that the inconvenience which Vickybird's litter-disposal caused to others was deliberately provocative. It was nothing of the sort. A psychoanalyst might describe it as 'compulsive,' but it was impulsive also, like most of his actions.

It was inevitable that my brother and I should seek out Vickybird as a friend. We had no companions of our own age, and all the other inhabitants of Steyning whom we knew conformed so perfectly well to their allotted rôles in the community that they grew after a time as monotonous as the characters in Happy Families, Mr Bun the Baker, and Mrs Chips the Carpenter's Wife.

Vickybird, on the other hand, was strange; and by our generation strangeness was accepted as a welcome and interesting quality in a way that it had not been by our parents. In the quarter of a century that separated us, unconventionality had become a convention accepted by a small but powerful minority to which my brother and I vehemently belonged.

Our parents still believed the assurance given by Long-fellow to the Victorians:

> Tell me not, in mournful numbers,
>   Life is but an empty dream!
>
> Life is real! Life is earnest!
>   And the grave is not its goal.

But to us, post-Freudians, 'empty' was no longer an epithet applicable to dreams. 'Earnest' was an adjective heavy with social disapproval ("Of course, Pamela is a charming girl, but isn't she just a wee bit earnest?"), and the highest term of praise was 'amusing.' People, pictures, statues made from wire and cobbler's wax, or a symphony calling for an orchestra including factory sirens, water-closets and field artillery were all in their several ways 'amusing' or 'rather fun.'

The liberties fought for and won over half a century by Ibsen, Bradlaugh, Darwin, Havelock Ellis, Samuel Butler, Freud, Wells, Shaw and a host of others with a deep moral purpose acting as a counterbalance to their revolutionary thinking, were being enjoyed by a generation avid for fun. The giants of the nineteenth century had stormed and taken the citadel of the Humbugs. The generations that reached their majority in the twenties sacked and looted it.

Looking back to that period, I find much that was wanton and silly, though it *was* 'rather fun' at the time. But there was also a lot of justification. The intellectual giants may have hewed a way through the jungle of myths and hypocrisies which had grown up through the smug period of capitalist expansion, but there was still plenty of dead wood to be cleared away. Hacking about us indiscriminately, we may have done a certain amount of harm, but nothing that was really alive failed to grow again.

I say this, not merely in explanation of my friendship with Vickybird, but so that any readers of this book born after 1918 may have some yardstick by which to measure it. In the twenties we looked back to the Mauve Decade of the nineties not with nostalgia, but with affection. We felt an affinity with the Restoration, with Pope, Donne, Swift and of course the Elizabethan dramatists. The great figure of the Romantic Revival was William Blake, not the Lake Poets, Byron, Keats or Shelley. It was an age of intellectual freedom, spiritual adventure and sexual licence. "Do what thou Wilt shall be the whole of the Law," Aleister Crowley might intone ad nauseam in his Cockney accent. But the new generation needed no liturgy to get cracking. It was eager for experiment because the old values of the nineteenth century, despite the intellectual bombardment of the artists and the catastrophe of the First World War, were still triumphant.

The class war during the twenties was being waged with acerbity. But at the same time that the ruling classes of England were fighting against the workers and the workless, they were being undermined by guerilla forces recruited from their own people. There was a running fight between the artists and the Philistines, with dirty tactics on both sides.

In Steyning, Vickybird held a solitary outpost, badly wounded and never, we suspected, a very effective fighter. But it was inevitable that we should join forces with him.

It was not at all difficult, because not even his worst

enemy accused him of being stand-offish. He bowed and he scraped and he grinned and he joked with anyone and everyone who would permit it.

> No! I am not Prince Hamlet, nor was meant to be;
> Am an attendant lord, one that will do
> To swell a progress, start a scene or two,
> Advise the prince; no doubt, an easy tool,
> Deferential, glad to be of use,
> Politic, cautious, and meticulous;
> Full of high sentence, but a bit obtuse;
> At times, indeed, almost ridiculous—
> Almost, at times, the Fool.

No, Vickybird was not J. Alfred Prufrock, but he chose to be, deferential, glad to be of use, at times indeed almost ridiculous—almost, at times, the Fool, if it suited his book. For some reason which eluded us, it usually did suit his book to play the Fool. It was only in motley that he could survive in the Philistine encampment of Steyning.

But why on earth was he in Steyning? Vine Cottage, we understood, was not his own. He lived there by courtesy of a rich aunt. But if the aunt was sympathetic enough to let him have this cottage, why wouldn't she agree to his letting the cottage and living on the rental somewhere more sympathetic to his talents? If Vickybird were really as miserable as he ought to have been, why didn't he sell some of his books, which even in those days were worth at least a thousand pounds, in order to secure his liberty?

It was a mystery.

But in his first term at Oxford my brother thought he had found the solution.

"Vickybird," he wrote me, "may be rated lowly in the quaint old-fashioned market town. But I can assure you that if my stock rates high in the House, it is on the strength of knowing him. In reputation he stands second only to The Beast 666 himself; is indeed a figure more fabulous, not, you may understand, by reason of those poems begotten by Pierre Louys out of Annie Besant, but of his metamorphosis, which out-assinizes Apuleius.

"In the first decade of the century, it appears that he went into the middle of the Sahara with Aleister Crowley and, drawing a circle in the sand, they summoned up the Devil.

"The Beast and the Devil tried to hold a serious business conversation, but Vickybird kept chipping in with questions of a purely 'ostrobogulous'* nature until Crowley became so enraged that he turned Vickybird into a zebra, rode him into Alexandria, and sold him to a zoo, where he remained for two years before regaining human shape.

"Any strangeness which we may observe in the Poet might be due to the fact that his resumption of the human form is not yet complete. I should like you, when you next see him, to watch out for zebra-like qualities. The *Encyclopædia Britannica*, as usual deficient on all important questions, has nothing to say about the psychology of zebras. It is worth noting, however, that the zebra stands about four foot at the shoulder, with fairly long ears, and the lower part of the face is brown. My recollection is that V.B's ears are fairly long, but Please Check.

---

* 'Ostrobogulous' was Vickybird's favourite word. It stood for anything from the bawdy to the slightly off-colour. Any *double entendre* that might otherwise have escaped his audience was prefaced by, 'if you will pardon the ostrobogulosity.'

"I remember that in your copy of his *Songs of the Groves* there was a poem purporting to be written by Lucius Apuleius in the person of the Golden Asse, imploring to be returned to human shape. Perhaps this is a thinly disguised excursion into autobiography.

"In that case, his reluctance to return to civilised society is explicable. I wonder what Apuleius himself did. You remember that terrifying story by Andreyev of Lazarus's reappearance after he had been raised from the dead, the walking, talking corpse? Apuleius never really tackled his problems of readjustment after regaining human shape. He probably had to spend the rest of his days in village retirement, considered by the yokels as rather an ass."

My brother had a flair for being inoffensively impudent. During his next vacation he tackled Vickybird on the truth of the story, choosing his ground carefully.

A few doors away from the Vine Press there was a small pub, called I think the Norfolk Arms, a Kemp Town Brewery House, kept in those days by an affable sportsman, whose father was affected by the most hideous distortion of the finger-joints I have ever seen, but both of whose daughters were comely in their different ways, the elder blonde and tall and gracious, the younger round and cosy, with a head covered in brown curls like Paris sausages.

It was to the Norfolk Arms, rather than our own home, that we bore Vickybird, when his wife made it plain that we had outstayed our welcome at the Vine Press.

Vickybird drank little, and this not purely from poverty. A half of bitter carried him a long way. Give him an inch to drink and it took him an ell to finish.

He would only come to the pub under persuasion, and he never bought a drink in return. "M.E.G.H.," he would say, raising his glass, "Most Extraordinary Good Health." But when his turn for a round came, he would finger his unfinished glass. "When my ship comes in," he said, "as indubitably it will one day—do not laugh, gentlemen—I shall buy you the other half."

We did not laugh, even though it was hard to imagine how his ship would come in, since he apparently had no craft afloat. Nor did we feel resentful that he never bought a drink, partly because it was plain that he came to the pub with us only because he enjoyed our company and would have preferred it without beer, and partly because, though poor, he was a man of consummate honesty. In a local antique shop there was displayed on sale an early and finely bound copy of the *Basilikon Doron* by King James I of Great Britain and Ireland, VI of Scotland. We pointed this out to Vickybird, who went in and asked the price.

"Ten bob," said the dealer.

"I won't buy it for ten bob," said Vickybird, "because it's worth at least five pounds. And I won't buy it for five pounds, because I haven't got five pounds. But don't sell it for less." As he was going out of the door, he turned round. "Why not ask six for it?"

Within a week the dealer had sold it for six pounds.

It was a strange facet of Vickybird's character, that for himself he would take no trouble but for others there was no trouble too great for him to take; in his own affairs he was foolish and quixotic, in his advice to friends, wise, shrewd and cautious.

I had never seen Vickybird angry with individual people. He hated Philistinism but found excuses for each individual Philistine; he inveighed against injustice, hypocrisy, smugness and wilful ignorance, but he never lost his temper with people.

That morning, however, when my brother asked him the truth of the zebra story, I expected to see an outburst of anger against the stupidity of undergraduates in general and the insensitiveness of my brother in particular. Instead he listened intently, with an occasional ejaculation, "Really!" "Most interesting!"

As a deliberate snub, it would have been effective; as the genuine expression of interest, it was mortifying. My brother scarcely dared to finish the story.

"I expect you'd like to know what really happened," Vickybird said, "because I can assure you that it is inaccurate in every detail; as well as in substance." He accepted a cigarette and lighted it, having at this moment of apology a triumphant dignity which sat upon him well. "In the first place," he said, "we did not go into the middle of the Sahara, but merely into the desert a few miles out of Marrakhesh. And we did not draw a circle, but a pentacle, which from a magical point of view is a very different matter." He paused, knowing that to us it was not the exact stretch of sand or the nature of the geometrical pattern which was of importance. "A pentacle, as there is no need to inform you, is a figure consisting of five straight lines crossing and joined so as to form a five-pointed star, which, as the Gnostics discovered, is a potent protection against the demons, or dæmons, of heavier essence, which inhabit the lower realms of heaven."

"But you did talk to a demon?" said my brother.

"It is impossible to 'talk' to elementals. They can be invoked by certain magic formulæ and equally they can be dispelled. It was as a protection against them that we drew the pentacle, while we talked with a spirit who wished to be known as P.472."

"He sounds," suggested my brother, "like an early motorist."

"He was," said Vickybird, calmly, "a foreman builder from Ur of the Chaldees, still earthbound."

The two daughters of the house were engrossed in their occupations, the tall blonde knitting a striking jumper, the plump curly-headed one reading the *Daily Mirror*. My brother tapped his tankard, signifying 'the same again.'

"That must have been very interesting," I said.

"So I thought at the time," Vickybird agreed, "but in retrospect I think not. After all, it stands to reason that for a spirit to remain earthbound so long, he must in life have been of an exceptionally heavy and base nature, almost indeed the sort of moron who becomes a poltergeist."

"You didn't ask him," said my brother, "how, if he was so moronic, he ever succeeded in becoming a foreman builder?"

"We did not," Vickybird answered; "we weren't really interested. And anyway you can never trust what they say about their earthly lives. They're terrible liars, most of them."

"Then what did you talk about?"

"Well, at first," said Vickybird, "we tried to get information out of him. You probably know that the

Valentinian School maintained that the material world was made not by Seven Powers but by a single Demiurge. We hoped P.472 would know whether this was true."

"After all," said my brother, looking me straight in the eye, "he'd had plenty of time."

"That's what we thought," Vickybird said, "but of course if he had risen as high as that, he wouldn't have been earthbound. It was a situation really rather absurd, because though we had summoned this spirit to learn more about the life beyond, we found that he was so ignorant that we already knew more than he did. It was he who was asking questions of us."

"What sort of questions?"

"There are names and formulæ and certain symbols revealed to the Gnostics that can secure passage to the higher realms of heaven of which this earth is the lowest plane," Vickybird explained, "and what knowledge we had we passed on to P.472, making him swear that he would return the next day, if it were spiritually possible, to tell us what lay at the limit of our knowledge. But though we went back the next day, and the day after that, he never returned."

"He doesn't sound a spirit you could trust," I said.

Vickybird shrugged his shoulders. "In this incarnation I shall never know. Perhaps he forgot or perhaps he was prevented."

"And no quarrel?" said my brother, "no zebra?"

"I only quarrelled once with Crowley, and that was final," Vickybird said. "Tell me, do I look as if I'd been a zebra?"

At that moment the door of the Norfolk Arms opened

and Vickybird's wife appeared. "Your lunch," she said, "was ready half an hour ago."

Instantaneously, as if by magic, the cap and bells returned. He got down from his stool and bowed deeply. "My ducky diamonds, my lady whiff," he said, "from the heart of my bottom, no, pardon my spoonerism, from the bottom of my heart, I tender thee the most apysmal abologies. Blame, if there blame must be, the cultured company of these two over-civilised, highly-educated young gentlemen, to wit Mr Robert Calder-Marshall *ex Aede Christi*, *Oxon*, commonly known as the House to its inmates and the Nuthouse to its exmates, likewise little Arthur of that ilk, author of that household work, *Little Arthur's History of England*, and many others with knobs on."

Beneath its cold mask of anger, his wife's face began to twitch at the corners of her mouth and then against her will she burst out laughing. "Come on, you ass," she said.

Chapter Two

The Poet 'At Home'

*

BOTH my parents disapproved of Vickybird on sight, his clothes, his face, shaven or unshaven, his patter, his alarming laugh and even his dog. He was decidedly not *their* sort of person.

What disquieted them was that my brother and I should regard him as *our* sort of person. Vickybird became the incarnation of all the traits in ourselves which caused uneasiness in their minds.

In retrospect I feel sorry for all parents whose children grew up during the twenties. Samuel Butler had raised the flag of infantile revolt against parents twenty years before. Yet even he had been frightened to publish *The Way of All Flesh* in his lifetime. That novel, written as a revenge against his parents, exploded like a delayed-action bomb * to make innumerable casualties in families unconceived at the time of its composition. A literary fashion was set. Edmund Gosse, in his *Father and Son*, dropped the pretence of fiction; and for twenty years childhoods of

* "People say how strong Public Opinion is; and indeed it is strong while it is in its prime. In its childhood and old age it is as weak as any other organism. I try to make my own work belong to the youth of a public opinion. The history of the world is the record of the weakness, frailty, and death of public opinion, as geology is the record of the decay of those bodily organisms in which opinions have found material expression!" Samuel Butler: *Notebooks*.

misery and misunderstanding were the vogue. It was as hard to find in fiction a pair of worthy parents as fifty years before it had been to find a pair of rotters.

The curious thing was that the generation which felt the brunt of this infantile attack was the first generation trying earnestly if not always successfully to understand their children, parents who to Samuel Butler would have appeared even in their blundering to be models of sympathy, kindliness, self-sacrifice and long-suffering.

Violence grows on what it feeds on. The greater the efforts that parents made to understand their children, the more difficult the children became to understand. It was small wonder that in their perplexity parents alternated between indulgence and Victorian asperity; small wonder also that in such a variable climate the emotional growth of the children was unbalanced.

Whereas today I recognise how much thought and love, as well as money, my parents invested in my future, in those days of thoughtless ingratitude I concentrated often more on what I couldn't have than on what I had; and whereas with every year I now recognise more clearly the inalienable ties of heredity, similarities between my mind, habit and character and those of my parents, at that time the desire to be an individual, rather than someone's child, was so strong that I refused to see that even this desire for uniqueness might be a direct inheritance from my father.

There must have been times when my brother and I during our adolescence appeared like vicious and ungrateful changelings rather than the dutiful sons my parents dreamed for. Caught into this war between the

artists and the Philistines, we enlisted enthusiastically in
the ranks of the artists, swallowing modernism at a gulp
and rejecting out of hand the moral and social values
which our parents hoped to imbue with us.

In this revolt against authority, my parents imagined
that Vickybird abetted us. The very opposite was true.
He encouraged our love of the arts, the free, irreverent
speculation which is the legitimate exercise of minds beginning to work for themselves. But he was careful to
point out to us, if we tried to win pity as poor misunder-
stood children, that our parents were equally misunder-
stood by us, and all the poorer for providing us with the
opportunities which were in part the cause of our misunderstanding. Standing midway between us in age and
on our side of the struggle, he was their ablest advocate.
There is little enough can be done with adolescents whose
real grievance is that they are not yet as old as they would
like to be. But Vickybird worked hard and tactfully in
my parents' service.

This made it all the stranger to hear my father inveigh-
ing against Vickybird. "I can't see what you find in that
grubby little man," he said. "He's unhealthy. He's a
crank. And I'm willing to bet you anything you like he's
introspective."

At this period of my father's life, introspection occu-
pied the seat of ultimate evil, which was later usurped by
Stalin. Introspection was the psychological aspect of the
Sin against the Holy Ghost.

"Your father," my mother would relay to us over the
breakfast table, after he had departed for the office (for
none of these pronouncements would come to us direct),

"your father has decided that you boys are far too intro-spective."

We made little attempt to defend Vickybird, because to have done so would have led us into one of the labyrinthine arguments in which my father was expert. Each tirade we met with the answer that if he wanted to find out what we saw in him, he should meet Vickybird himself.

"I don't want to meet the fellow," my father would answer. "I've better ways of spending my week-ends."

It seemed like an infallible method of avoiding an unprofitable conversation, until one Sunday morning my father replied, "All right, we will go and see him then. We will go and see him this morning."

"Are you quite sure you really want to go?" my brother asked.

"Why not?" asked my father. "You've been badgering me to meet him for the last year."

We had never mentioned to Vickybird the possibility of a parental call, because the prospect was so remote. For a moment my brother and I were in a panic. It was almost impossible to visualise them together in a room. They were as unmixable as oil and water, as antipathetic as dog and cat.

If the meeting had to take place, it was better it should be at Vine Cottage than at our house. Vickybird would after all be playing on his home ground. But even so I felt sorry for him, because my father on the warpath was a formidable opponent, and it was plain that he intended by humiliating the Poet to prove to us how tawdry and childish this artistic nonsense of ours was.

This appreciation of the position reassured me. If it was merely another battle in the war against our artistic nonsense, it would end as always, in my father's verbal victory, a strategic retreat and a consolidation behind new lines. It would be a pleasant change to sit back and watch Vickybird do the fighting instead of us.

There was no telephone at Vine Cottage, so we could not warn the Poet of our visitation. My father had gained the advantage of tactical surprise. But forewarned, Vickybird would not have been forearmed. He would have gone out for a long walk.

There was no one in Church Street when we walked down it at half-past eleven. The pious were at Mattins, the impious in bed. We could see no one through the windows of Vine Cottage, and when we hammered on the door, the noise caught in the street was echoed back so loudly that my father glanced furtively around him. Though the author of this expedition, he had no wish to be seen visiting the Poet.

Just as we were turning away a dim form appeared in the subfusc living-room, like a shark in the depths of an aquarium tank. There was a muffled oath as the figure tripped over a low table, a scrabbling at the door and Vickybird opened it, blinking his eyes against the blinding sunlight. There was thick stubble on his face and the dusty cuffs of flannel pyjamas protruded below the grey flannels which I had given him some weeks before. Two fly-buttons were undone and a bunion on his left foot protruded through his fawn felt carpet slippers.

In his first moment of blindness one could read only perplexity and annoyance on his face; but when his vision cleared, as on a print in a developing dish, there appeared an image of horror.

"I'm sorry," said my brother; "it isn't really the time to have called." But even as he and I began to disengage ourselves, Vickybird recovered his poise and making a deep salaam like the Grand Vizier in an amateur performance of *Ali Baba and the Forty Thieves*, said, "It is indeed an honour that so eminent a merchant from the great city of London should deign, accompanied by his two distinguished sons, to visit the abode of a humble bard at so auspicious an hour on this day of Phoebus. Prithee enter, gentle sirs. My house is yours."

He stood aside and extended his arm towards the living-room, which had not been tidied since the night before. Never was host or house less equipped for a visit; and Vickybird's insistence that we should come in was a fine instance of social jiu-jitsu that threw even my father momentarily off balance.

Though he entered, it was not in triumph. For the half-drawn curtains, the dirty ashtrays, the crumpled cushions and even the protruding pyjamas were, now that we had accepted his hospitality, somehow to Vickybird's credit.

"T.A.P.," said Vickybird, "Take a Pew." It was one of his routine abbreviations, of which the W.O.G. or Will of God was another. My father, less used to abbreviation in those days than he became during the Second World War, looked slightly startled, but then sat down heavily in the most comfortable armchair.

There was a shrill screech. My father started up as if he had received a load of buckshot in the seat. With a scrabble of claws, a flash of fur shot from under him, across the floor and out into the street.

"You must forgive her," Vickybird said, pulling back the curtains; "the familiars sleep late after the Sabbath."

My brother and I exchanged glances. Considering the disadvantages of tactical surprise, the Poet was doing well.

But with the return of light my father was getting his bearings. He bent down and picked up a brassière on which the cat had been lying. He held it up at arm's length. "What would you like me to do with this?"

"Do As thou Wilt shall be the whole of the Law!" said Vickybird, taking it from him, and examining it at a distance. "What a wonderful invention is the brassière. Contributory to far more pleasure than the gas-filled airships of Count Zeppelin. Incapable of dropping any but the sweetest of bombs. The inventor's name shall be mentioned in the Honours List of the Almighty." He tossed it on a pile of books.

At this moment his wife came down the stairs. Like Vickybird, she was Jewish, but of the type called Portuguese, with straight, jet-black hair and a dark complexion coloured red on the cheekbones. Her jaws were protrusive. When her generous lips were closed, she was as lovely as a peony. But when she spoke, she exposed large white teeth and pink gums more prominently than was modish at that time.

Her large, brown eyes were lustrous, but the thick lenses which she wore to remedy astigmatism enlarged them until they were out of proportion to her face.

Just as when women with long, elaborately coiffured hair remove the combs and pins and let it fall naturally about their shoulders, they seem to alter not only their appearance but also their character, so on the rare occasions when the Poet's wife removed her spectacles, not only did her face compose itself into the placid beauty, the vegetable exuberance of the peony bloom, but her character also appeared happier and untormented.

We become to an extent what we appear to be. Short-sightedness had forced on her spectacles which made her appear to someone looking through them the wrong way a splintered personality, a placid face and body from which stared eyes and a soul, almost hysterical for escape.

As soon as she came in, my father rose from his chair and shook her hand with more warmth than he had shown to her husband. What was not always customary in Vine Cottage, he remained standing until she was seated and he concentrated his conversation upon her. Many of their visitors came to see Vickybird and paid her perfunctory attention.

As a consulting engineer and merchant, my father had travelled widely. He was, I believe, a shy young man. But in the course of his travels he built up a repertory of anecdotes in every continent except Australia, which makes him one of the most fluent anecdotalists I have met. His talk is like a hydrant, normally untapped but which, when turned on full, can extinguish any spark of conversation.

"The secret," he once explained to me, "is that while you are telling one story, you select, according to the company, the one that is going to follow, so that you can Indulge in a Continuous Flow."

This continuous flow my father played on the Poet's wife, leaving the rest of us who were used to conversation, argument and gossip, at the sort of disadvantage which Stephen Potter would be the first to appreciate. It was a Blitzploy of Talesmanship. The subtlety of it was my father's implication that Vine Cottage was their house, that they had a private income and if they wanted to go to Luxor for the winter they could.

"You haven't given Mr Marshall anything to drink," said Kathleen to her husband.

"I don't think there is any coffee," Vickybird said. "You remember we forgot to get any yesterday."

I felt just a tiny bit ashamed of him for saying "You remember we forgot," when he meant "You know perfectly well that today's the 27th and the allowance isn't paid in till the first of the month."

But Kathleen was intoxicated with my father's talk of the High Andes, Calcutta, Shanghai and Petersburg. "I don't think that at this time Mr Marshall really wants coffee," she said. "What about beer?"

Vickybird looked at an antique clock which had stopped at eleven o'clock, probably a hundred years before. "The pub isn't open," he said.

"Really!" said his wife. "We have beer in the cellar."

"Oh, I'm sorry, I forgot," said Vickybird. "Now, who wants beer?"

"I certainly don't," said my brother. "You know I never drink before lunch."

"It makes me sleepy," I said.

"You surprise me," said my father. "But I think I'll have some. Now where was I?"

"Karachi," said Kathleen.

"The Crewe of Asia," my brother muttered.

There are so many of my father's stories which have Karachi as a *point d'appui* that I have forgotten which this was; indeed I am now as incapable of remembering stories about Karachi as about men from Buffalo. But it was obviously a good one, because when it came to an end Kathleen laughed heartily. Then she turned to Vickybird and asked him tartly where the beer was.

"That, my little cabbage, my turtle, was the question I was about to ask you."

"Where should it be except in the wine-cellar?" Kathleen said.

It was news to me that there was a wine-cellar at Vine Cottage. It seemed to be news also to Vickybird. He appeared bewildered.

"You know," said his wife. "It's just next door to the Marsala." She spoke with such authority that my brother and I believed for a moment that all this talk about Vickybird's ship coming in concealed the fact that it had made landfall without our knowledge.

"Of course," the Poet said, snapping his fingers as if he'd been a silly fool, though his expression showed that she had. He went out at the back towards the woodshed.

"If there *is* Marsala," said my father, "I *would* prefer that."

From the way in which Kathleen said, "I'm not sure," and then called out, "Vicky, if we didn't finish that last bottle of Marsala the other morning, Mr Marshall would prefer it," I realised what a lot she would have made out of even the most modest literary success, or for that matter another quid a week. Reputation, at least in a lifetime, is so much a question of economics.

Vickybird came back with a quart bottle of beer, half full, in one hand and in the other a toothglass. He held the toothglass up to the light. It was rather smeary, but my father didn't notice, because he had started telling us about a journey from Moscow to Vladivostok. This apparently takes four and a half days or months, I can never remember which. But my father had reached one of the high spots of the trip, a conversation with a kulak on the banks of Lake Baikal, by the time that Vickybird, accepting the bourgeois standards of finickiness which he normally scoffed at, was polishing the toothglass with the first thing to hand, his wife's brassière.

The Kulak got off the train at Bukachacha.

"How lucky you two boys are to have such an interesting father," Kathleen said. "I must say I envy you."

Interrupted in his smooth, relentless narrative, my father noticed that Vickybird was shaking the bottle of beer as if it were a cocktail. "There's nothing worse," explained Vickybird, "than beer without a head on it. But prithee continue, gentle sir."

My father did. The grand climax of his trip was in the terminus of Vladivostok station, a climax which over the years had become more and more powerful, and he was naturally reluctant to abandon any story in mid-course. He resumed his journey with a Ukrainian mining engineer working at the Tetiuhe Silver Mines.

During my father's conversation with the mining engineer, Vickybird poured him a glass of beer. "There is no Marsala," he murmured; "we finished it the Christmas before last."

Kathleen was leaning forward, listening to the way the mining engineer was being convicted out of his own mouth of a folly I have forgotten.

Only my brother and I looked at the toothglass of beer.

Any beer-drinker knows that, when it is allowed to stand for some time, bottled beer starts by developing white specks, like small dots of goats'-milk cheese, and then round the bottle, especially at the base, grow the sorts of semi-transparent culture found in ponds, either adhering to the stems of water-lilies or being trailed round by ardent golden carp in pursuit of a swollen female.

My father's glass of beer had no head, but it had all these other manifestations of life in it. As he reached the Amur River he raised the glass.

"M.E.G.H.," said Vickybird, encouragingly, "Most Extraordinary Good Health."

My father is a keen observer of pond and river life. When he was in Egypt, he sent my mother every week samples of Nilotic mud, from which she washed and separated shells. She isolated several snails which had never been found before and which, I was told in childhood, would have brought immortality to our family name, if they hadn't all been smashed by the Museum to which they were sent.

Raising his glass, my father must have felt as surprised as my mother had been at her first present of Nilotic mud. Vickybird rushed forward and took the toothglass. "There seems to be a little something," he said, and with the delicacy born of this visitation he fished for the long gelatinous threads and hard white flecks, not with his index finger but his little finger.

"Vickybird," his wife said, "please remember your manners. Can't you use a fountain pen?"

"I don't really feel thirsty," said my father, "but before we go, I think I ought to tell you a little story about when I was going through the Red Sea in 1912."

It was short; it was witty and well told. We all laughed as we went towards the door. Vickybird salaamed as we left and his wife wrung my father's hand. "This has been a real treat, Mr Marshall," she said. "You *must* come round again and tell us some more."

"I feel very thirsty," my father said, as we got into the street. "Don't you boys really drink before lunch?"

We said we could make an exception in his favour if he insisted, and took him into the pub next door but one. As the landlord's pretty daughter with the sausage curls drew three pints of bitter, my father said, "What an *impossible* little man! I can't understand how that girl puts up with him."

Kathleen, though I never told my father, was not finding it easy to put up with Vickybird. They had a small son, and as the boy grew, expenses mounted, but their income remained at its same abysmal level.

It is a measure of her desperation that though she regarded me as a callow youth and Vickybird's friend, not hers, Kathleen sometimes turned, in the rare moments when we were alone together, even to me for help, or more precisely consolation, since neither of us could see any prospect of rescue.

"It's all very well his saying he's a poet and that I'm a bourgeoise," she said. "But what does he do for the family? He doesn't even write poetry any longer; which is perhaps as well, because then he would want to print it, and that would be so much more money down the drain. All he does really is take the dog for a walk and buy the food, while I stay at home, do all the housework, make my own clothes, look after the boy, darn his socks. Bourgeoise, my eye! I belong to the domestic proletariat."

I opened my mouth to utter condolence and then closed it again, ashamed to fob her off with inanities.

"You can see for yourself, Arthur. It's not fair. It's asking too much of any woman to expect her to carry on like this."

"I know," I said, "I know. But what can I do?"

"You may not realise it," she said, "but you've got quite an influence over him. He's very fond of you."

"You know I'd do anything to help you all," I said, flattered that anybody of her mature age should think I could be of assistance, but at the next moment depressed by the recognition of my impotence. "If you could only suggest something."

She got up and resumed her dusting. "It's no use," she said. "He wouldn't take it from you either; any more than he does from his family. It needs someone he respects, but his own age, to tell him to pull himself together. Good Lord, he's not the only poet who's had a family to support!"

Vickybird himself never discussed his relations with Kathleen, at any rate openly. When my brother left Oxford for Columbia University, I spent practically every week-day of the holidays with Vickybird, going for long walks over the Downs or by the river towards Henfield. On these walks he never stopped talking even when tidying the countryside, but he was seldom talking to me. He used me rather as a lonely child will use a wall for tennis practice. I returned his shots with little idea of what he was up to.

Though his desperation was no less acute than Kathleen's, it was of a different essence. His concern with money or the future of his family was remote.

"I see for you," he would say to engage my interest, "a future in the arts, my little Arthur—did Mrs Markham really write that history for you, I wonder?—as brilliant as your brother's as a scientist. And I envy you; as a Failure, I envy you. Because, you know, I am a Failure. And yet there was a time, believe it or, an you will, believe it not, when I was one of the brightest contributors to a periodical called the *New Age*, edited by the redoubtable Orage, in its day as good a paper and in some ways in my opinion better than the *New Statesman* which you read so avidly each Friday. Ah me! How are the flighty fallen!"

"But you aren't old," I would comfort, wondering to myself how much younger than my father he was in years and how much older in vigour.

"Have you thought to yourself," he would go on to himself, "that there's a periodicity in men as there is in women? There is much to be said for the Seven Year

Cycle. We relive the drama of human evolution in the womb. Once we are born, that drama is not ended.

> Grown old in love, from seven till seven times seven
> I oft have wished for Hell, for ease from Heaven."

He had no desire to confide in me. But if he had wanted to, he could not have done so. His brain was enmeshed and what I observed was merely his struggle to escape.

I have seen a rabbit wounded in one leg that could continue to run with speed almost unchecked, but whose course became a frantic circle. That was how Vickybird's mind would race at times, lap after lap of the same track, as we walked beside the river with his fat bitch galoomphing after moorhens.

Over and over again the same thoughts, or more accurately the same sequence of words, would issue from his mouth, like a commentary being run through repeatedly on a movieola, except that the volume and the emphasis varied.

At first my main feeling was annoyance, because there is no surer way of showing someone that his presence is unimportant than to say the same thing to him five or six times. It is far more effective than surly silence.

Then I became frightened for Vickybird. I accepted him as in some respects a trifle barmy. But this was different. He was, in so far as he was in control of the steering-wheel, deliberately driving himself mad.

The more that Kathleen tried to force him to face reality, the more acrimonious the scenes with his family on his monthly visits to Hove to report progress, the more desperately he buried his head in the contemplation of Success and Failure and the periodicity of Genius.

I asked him why he didn't return to London, why if he was faced with a period of poetic sterility he didn't turn to prose. But these questions only made things worse, drove him deeper into his dark burrow of frustration.

"At least," he once said, when he seemed to have reached a terminus of self-abasement, "I have never failed to satisfy a woman sexually; I can go on and on."

Unconsciously I hit on something which helped to restore his self-respect. Vickybird discovered my admiration for Blake's *Songs of Innocence and Experience* and it was he who introduced me to his Ideas of Good and Evil. He took me through *The Everlasting Gospel*, *The Mental Traveller*, *The Marriage of Heaven and Hell*. He opened the door to a garden filled with the sort of beauty and wisdom which at that moment I most needed.

The fragility of happiness had always haunted me, the way that the pleasures most eagerly anticipated are the least enjoyed, and the most remembered are moments of unplanned delight, when the occasion, like a wave, takes one riding on its surf to an unsuspected beach.

> He who bends to himself a joy
> Does the winged life destroy;
> But he who kisses the joy as it flies
> Lives in eternity's sunrise.
>
> If you trap the moment before it's ripe,
> The tears of repentance you'll certainly wipe;
> But if once you let the ripe moment go
> You can never wipe off the tears of woe.

I had already fallen in love with the work of many writers, either fleetingly or with an enduring passion. But to none have I felt such gratitude, such an intimate

warmth, as Blake. Though he is regarded as a mystic, he
seemed to me then as now merely a writer of dazzling
honesty and common sense. His metaphors, paradoxes
and proverbs are only as complex as the human experience
which he describes.

With Vickybird for master, I studied Blake mornings
and afternoons. He invested even the trivial events and
contrasts of my life with deeper meaning.

The Vine Press was the nearest house to the church,
where the vicar pursued his low church duties while his
wife was denouncing Vickybird as the anti-Christ.

> The vision of Christ that thou dost see
> Is my vision's greatest enemy: . . .
> Thine is the friend of all Mankind,
> Mine speaks in Parables to the blind,
> Thine loves the same world that mine hates,
> Thy heaven-doors are my hell-gates.
> Socrates taught what Melitus
> Loathed as a nation's bitterest curse.
> And Caiaphas was in his own mind
> A benefactor to mankind.
> Doth read the Bible day and night,
> But thou readst black where I read white.

It was, I perceive, the same technique of thinking as my
grandfather had pursued in the village Sunday School
with his drunken blacksmith of Bramfield: though the
philosophy was different. I saw the vicar walking down
the street being agreeable to everyone who attended the
Parish Church and chilly to the people who went to the
Chapel. And I saw Vickybird giving the snotty-nosed
girl a shining halfpenny and telling the secondhand dealer
about the *Basilikon Doron*. I witnessed the Justice of the
Peace sentencing to six months' imprisonment for stealing
a shilling an old lag whose first offence had been taking a

cabbage out of a field fifty years before and his first sentence a year in jail. And I witnessed the Poet giving a tramp sixpence with the vicar's wife watching him narrowly from across the street.

> He mock'd the Sabbath, and He mock'd
> The Sabbath's God, and He unlock'd
> The evil spirits from their shrines,
> And turn'd fishermen to divines.

To the narrow struggles of the quaint old-fashioned market town Blake brought illumination.

What had appeared ephemeral and mean now embodied an eternal conflict between good and evil. I was conscious of a blinding light of revelation, a desire to dedicate myself to the inner truth and beauty glimpsed in the gnomic verses. But I realise now that through teaching me Vickybird was regaining spiritual strength and confidence.

At times his brain still lost its balance and stood swaying dizzily on the edge of madness; but less frequently. He talked with assurance and hope. Even his exile in Steyning appeared splendid. "The path of wisdom lies through excess," he would say. "If the fool shall persist in his folly, he will become wise." And he would laugh that sudden, alarming laugh. "Yes, we are entering into a new phase."

But the new phase made no change in the Poet's fortune. He was happier, saner; but he still wrote nothing, made no money.

Kathleen announced her own plan of action. If every retired cook on Castle Hill could keep her family by letting rooms in summer, why shouldn't she do the same?

Or rather, not quite the same, because in those days to let rooms was regarded as socially degrading. To have boarders was lower class. So Kathleen took P.G.'s or, to give them their full title, Paying Guests, who lived and ate with the family as guests would, but paid a little more than boarders did. "If the house gets too full," she said to her husband, "you can always go to the Sanctuary."

Kathleen had become resigned to Vickybird's drone-like existence. If he was quiet and happy, that was the best that she could hope for. But as she lifted the economic burden on to her own shoulders, she could not prevent a tinge of contempt creeping into her voice. "After all, you enjoy yourself at the Sanctuary."

In our part of West Sussex, the Sanctuary had a reputation even more lurid than Vine Cottage had in Steyning. Occasionally the local papers carried a story of one of the Sanctuaryites appearing before the magistrates for being drunk in Storrington and uttering an obscene word to a police constable. But it was what happened within the Sanctuary that was the main topic of speculation. Long-haired young men in sandals could be seen walking with short-haired young women in dirndls, and it was whispered that not all the couples there were married. At that time even the thought of young men with long hair would induce a state of fury bordering on apoplexy in certain people, especially those on whose walls hung reproductions of paintings showing Jesus Christ as a young man with long hair. Against the Sanctuary were directed all the batteries of abuse. The Sanctuaryites were Bolsheviks, atheists, diet-cranks, nudists, contraceptionists, scum, if one was to believe the local Pharisees.

If, on the other hand, one listened to Vickybird, the Sanctuary was one of the great artistic settlements of the time, a place where, thanks to the bounty of the Queen ("a P.P., Perfect Pet, you know"), the cream of the intelligentsia was to be found, writers, painters, musicians, philosophers as well as those known vaguely as 'progressives.' And when I hinted to him that popular conception was very different, he tersely quoted, "A fool sees not the same tree that a wise man sees."

The tree or rather trees (for the colony was planted in woodland) that I saw, when at last I visited the Sanctuary with Vickybird, were different from either his or the Pharisees'. I was impressed not by the intellectual or artistic brilliance of the gathering but by the appropriateness of the title Sanctuary. It was an asylum for almost every type of refugee, not a workshop for those who found life in the city too distracting. "Rather than be driven to this," I said to myself, "I'll starve in a garret."

Yet I appreciated why Vickybird loved it so. His whole manner changed as we boarded the bus and drew out of Steyning. He sang *Johnny Hall* and chattered like a schoolboy going on holiday.

In Steyning, when he was indoors he was the drone-like father; and when he went down the street he was the mad Poet. But in the Sanctuary he and the Queen held court like Oberon and Titania. He was a visiting potentate, a poet whose poems had actually been published, a publisher who actually published poems. The stacks of unsold copies of *Lillygay*, *Swift Wings* and *Songs of the Groves* were forgotten in the admiration of writers, even less successful than he, who gathered round to greet him.

In founding her colony the Queen had had a vision which must at times have grown blurred and dim. But when Vickybird began to talk, he so appreciated what she had intended to do, was so eager to believe that she had done it, that for a moment he succeeded in convincing them all that it was a fact, that in this asylum to which they had fled through one weakness or another they had chosen a noble retirement. Reality faded as he elaborated the dream, tossing his curly hair back from his forehead and gazing into the darkening sky with the coal of his cigarette proclaiming dusk.

As I listened, I was caught by his fire, and it no longer seemed to me strange that he should be living in Steyning, afraid apparently to venture back to London. I forgot his inability to write, his humble shopping expeditions, his desperation. All I was conscious of was the Poet's devotion to his art, the self-immolation without which great art is impossible and even with which it is rare.

Chapter Three
The See-er

*

WHEN the time came for me to go to Oxford, Vickybird was insistent that I should call on his old
friend, 'Auntie Helen.' "She really is a pet," he said;
"though not a poet or in any sense a 'maker,' she is a true
'see-er.'"

Though I had grown to value Vickybird's friendship in
the loneliness of Steyning, I was not certain that I wanted
to desert the brilliant company of my fellow undergraduates to seek out an old woman whom Vickybird had
known in what he described as 'those wonderful days in
Chelsea before the War,'—however true a see-er she
might be.

Through reading Oscar Wilde and *Zuleika Dobson* I
had conceived a fantastic idea of the University, a dream
of wit and brilliance which had not been dimmed but en-
hanced by my brother's period of residence there. As well
as being an outstanding scientist, my brother was bright
and gay and very sharp in his general intelligence. Even
his worst jokes seemed brilliant to me, four years his
junior, and I imagined that all my fellow freshmen would
have a sophistication equal to that which my brother had
acquired by the time he went down.

What sort of a figure I should cut in this glittering
throng I was most doubtful. "Just a wee bit earnest" was

my brother's comment on my character. In a world where 'Fun' was king, I secretly admitted to myself I wouldn't shine; and though I had read more widely than most undergraduates, I realised the superficiality of my knowledge. There seemed a danger that among the flippant I would be too grave and among the grave too flippant.

Oxford itself was a city so beautiful and so resplendent in the glory of the great men who had studied there that at first I wandered round, sensible only of my unworthiness beneath the grandeur of the past. The young men, bowling down the Broad on bikes, hustling from lecture to lecture in the morning, and in the afternoon walking beside the river in excited conversation, could, provided that one did not come too close, fit into the pageant of Oxonian greatness. Only I was an absurd exception, an unworthy impostor.

Then as the freshness of freshmanship wore off, when the crowds of scholarly faces came into focus and I began to learn the names to which these faces answered, I discovered the hollowness of my dream. Callow and silly as I was, most of my fellows were even sillier and more callow. Not I alone, but all of us were impostors in this noble seat of learning, unworthy of the buildings where we lived and studied.

I felt a revulsion against my fellow undergraduates for not playing the parts I had allotted them, for being so obviously ex-school-captains, ex-prefects or ex-monitors. I sneered at the eager, and yes! "earnest," way they were learning to grow into undergraduates. I became aware and proud of my superior sophistication. I associated as much as possible with contemporaries of my brother who had remained up to take post-graduate courses.

I realise now that what I then considered the advantage of my brother preceding me at Oxford was a grave disadvantage. I had learned too much from him at second-hand; had lost my innocence without the emotional experiences that compensate for its loss. Without intending to, I had become the typical early-Aldous-Huxley young man, precocious in intellect but in experience a child. My sour appraisal of my fellow freshmen was tinged with envy.

This was the mood in which I turned to Auntie Helen. Her age, which I had considered such a drawback, was now an advantage. Even an old bitch was preferable to this litter of puppies.

I wrote a note to her address in Ship Street, telling her that I was a friend of Vickybird's and would like to call.

The next morning I received a heather-coloured envelope of hand-laid bond with deckle edges, of a quality now used only by Foreign Embassies and new publishing firms which have not yet established their position. On the back was a monogram so intricately designed that its component letters were indecipherable. Not so my name and address, which staggered in gigantic purple letters across the front.

Both the envelope and the letter it contained were heavily impregnated with chypre.

The letter was an invitation to tea on the following day, conventional except for the reasons added for the selection of that date, "because it is early closing day and the stars are right."

Couched in such terms, the request was impossible to refuse. Crowley might design the most bizarre surroundings for his rites, but I am most susceptible to magic amid the commonplace. I remember once, when on a walk by myself across the Downs between Steyning and Lancing, I came upon a valley which I had never seen before. It was narrower than most in the Sussex hills, with abrupt sides and tangled with coarse grass from which as I descended rabbits bolted momently like small brown explosions.

It ran from west to east in a winding course and I knew that, if I followed it downward, I should at last come on to the Bramber–Lancing road and the broad valley of the Adur. I knew this, and yet as I stumbled over the rank tufts with only rabbits for company and high above in the blue a singing lark, tossed like a scrap of paper glinting in the sun, there came to me a suspicion which grew with alarming speed into a conviction that, when I reached the last turn in the valley, I should look not on the green meadows of the Adur but on the blue sea.

At first I was filled with strange excitement. I began to run forward, jumping from tuft to tuft. I thought I could hear distant waves breaking on a pebbled beach, sucking shingle down as they receded. I caught in my nostrils the sharp tang of salt. My heart exulted with miraculous delight.

Then I tripped and fell face forward in the grass; and as I lay winded, testing my twisted ankle, a thought came to me which converted joy to terror.

There *had been* sea at the mouth of that valley once. But that was centuries ago. Had I in this steep, unusual valley, teeming with rabbits, somehow fallen through a pocket in time?

I listened and the noise of breakers now was quite distinct, as if the shore was just round the next bend. I had merely to go another hundred yards to see it for myself.

But fear caught me. I got up and started climbing the steep wall of grass, clutching at tufts with my fingers to prevent myself falling; and I didn't stop until I reached the flat top of the hill, where I flung myself on the short cropped turf, breathless but safe in the twentieth century with the lark still trilling overhead.

I thought later that I had been a fool, a coward; and the next day I set out for the valley again, telling myself that I should allay my fears by discovering where it ended, but in reality wanting to experience again that feeling of primeval terror descending from the urbane pasture into that wild ravine.

But neither of my aims was satisfied. Though I searched then and often afterwards, I never found that valley again.

This digression from Auntie Helen and Ship Street is not as irrelevant as it may seem. For though Ship Street appeared as commonplace a thoroughfare as you could find in the centre of Oxford, I had already discovered that it was no ordinary street, in that it housed Mr James Brown, Wine Merchant.

Sometimes today in London streets I see a van belonging to James Brown (Oxford) Ltd, Wines and Spirits. There are three branches in London, one in Mayfair, a second in Soho and a third, curiously, at 1415 London

Road, S.W.16. These must, I suppose, have some connection with that homely and obscure establishment in Ship Street which a quarter of a century ago supplied me with amber ale at fifteen shillings the $4\frac{1}{2}$ gallon pin and a good Amontillado at four and sixpence a bottle. Yet it is hard to associate a multiple wine store with the Dickensian vintner of Ship Street, whom I took, perhaps erroneously, to be Mr Brown himself.

Not unlike Mr Punch to look at, he had a long, perennially red nose, on the end of which, as with a tap whose washer has just begun to perish, a bead of moisture would imperceptibly form and grow to fullness. Then, just as it was about to fall, up would go his clean white handkerchief.

Mr Brown had a voice like that of a cathedral verger, deep and yet hushed, unperturbed by Births, Deaths or Marriages. Yet in his rheumy eyes there was a glint of schoolboy naughtiness; and when he was amused he laughed inside himself, like a blacksmith's bellows.

He welcomed undergraduates into his dim office as if they were old family clients come to lay down a pipe of port for their grandchildren. He assumed in his customers a connoisseurship which he proceeded to cultivate by giving them the information they needed as if they had already had it. Even if you popped in to buy a bottle of sherry, the old œnophile would detain you. "Could you spare a moment, sir? I have received a new consignment of Beaune which you would appreciate. You must try it, sir. I insist." Then he would disappear into the back of the shop and return with a bottle and a glass. As you drank, he stood leaning forward with his hands splayed over the counter, his body intent and immobile as he watched the progress of the good wine down your gullet; and then, as it set out on its beneficent journey through your system, he would analyse the sensations it was creating almost as if not you, but he, had drunk it.

He felt, I am sure, that his function was as important as any in this seat of learning; that wine had contributed more to the good life than metaphysics, and that while the nature of the Good, the True and the Beautiful would always be a matter for argument, there could be no dispute about the nature of a good vintage.

Auntie Helen lived on the opposite side of the street to Mr James Brown, in every sense of the phrase. All they had in common was a deceptive exterior. No one would have suspected that such wisdom and good cheer lay behind the musty windows of the vintner's shop, or that three floors above the routine display of flannel trousers, plus-fours and college wear in the tailor's window was a ménage as strange as Auntie Helen's.

The staircase I ascended that auspicious early-closing day was as bare and comfortless as any in an Oxford College, except that on the doors were names not of undergraduates but of firms. It was so unlike a dwelling-house that, when I got half-way up, I descended again to make sure that I had got the right number. But immediately I saw the outside of Auntie Helen's door, I knew that I was right.

When I told her this later, she said that it was a sign that we were spiritually *en rapport*. What I had perceived was an emanation of her aura. This pleased me, because, like many young men uncertain of their true powers, I was flattered at the attribution even of false ones. But I had the honesty to admit to myself that it was not Auntie Helen's aura that convinced me that I had come to the right place, but the large bronze lantern of Moorish design which loomed above the door. It was in keeping with the heather note-paper, the monogram, the scent of chypre.

The lantern was not lit and it was dark at the head of the stairs. I felt the door for a knocker but my fingers encountered only a wrought-iron grille. I lit a match and saw that to one side of the door was a heavy metal knob cast in the form of a bull's head. Taking it by the horns, I tugged, and from where I was I heard a peal which to anyone inside must have been deafening.

I blushed, expecting someone to come running, muttering "All right, all right, I'm coming!" But there was no noise of footsteps, a quiet so deep that I became conscious of my own breathing.

I waited for what seemed two or three minutes irresolute. I could not ring the bell again. It would be like shouting in a cathedral. There seemed nothing for it but to go away. And I was rather glad. I could say to Vickybird, "I called on your Auntie Helen, as you told me to. She asked me for tea when the shops were closed and the stars were right. But she never opened the door to me."

As I turned to go, I heard a slight sound. Behind the grille, a panel was being slid back. A hole about the size of a half-crown appeared, lit by the light within. Then the hole grew darker, but peering forward I caught a fleck of light in the pupil of an eye. It stared for a moment unwinking. Then the panel slid into position again and a red light snapped on in the Moorish lantern above my head. Massive bolts were pulled back, creaking in their sockets, and the door swung open.

Standing in the shadows of the hallway was a tall, stately woman, dressed in a long black velvet gown. Suddenly she stretched forward her arms, and in her cold white hands, heavy with barbaric rings, she caught mine. "So you have come, my young friend," she said. "Welcome."

Before I could recover poise, she yanked me across the threshold, shut the door, slammed the bolts to and took a hurried quiz through the spyhole to see that no one had followed me.

I had the sense of being admitted into a beleaguered fortress with enemy cavalry, brandishing drawn sabres, or perhaps a howling horde of Fuzzy Wuzzies, at my heels.

Yet, as she came towards me, she made no allusion to her strange behaviour. "You must pardon the squalor of my attic," she said, "but then of course, if you're a friend of Vicky's, you're an artist and know that only tradesmen live in palaces today." She spoke in a deep, tragic voice, resonant with emotion. I could imagine her in *Phèdre*, bringing the house to its feet, cheering. But in a hallway no larger than a cubicle in a gramophone shop, she was overpowering.

She opened a door into a large room. There was a noise of scuffling, and something long and thin and brown streaked past, pursued by something equally long and thin and brown. "You like mongooses, don't you?" she asked, or rather stated, because she waited for no answer.

The only mongoose I had met previously bit me deeply in the finger, and my opinion was that the sooner all mongooses were exported to places plagued with snakes and rats, the happier the world would be; an opinion which my experience with Auntie Helen's pair did nothing to modify. But I had no chance of voicing it, because she caught me by the shoulders and staring into my eyes asked, "What are you?"

At that moment I didn't know whether I was a man or a mouse. I was conscious only of two greeny-yellow eyes which appeared to be focused at the back of my brain.

"I'm afraid I don't quite understand."

Annoyance passed like the shadow of a hand across her face. "I mean, under what sign? When were you born?"

"I was born under Leo."

"Like Napoleon! Like Julius Cæsar! The sign of greatness! I might have guessed it."

She must, I thought, have been a very beautiful woman when she was young. Even now, with her height and slenderness accentuated by the long black gown, her tawny hair bound with a broad fillet of python-skin, she was strikingly handsome.

"You must tell me the exact minute of your birth," she said; "I will cast your horoscope."

Then I realised that as a woman she could never have been beautiful. She had the magnificence of one of the larger cats, a panther, or a leopardess. For any normal woman that attic, which was the depth and almost the breadth of the house with its high rafters meeting in semi-darkness twenty feet above the floor, would have provided an ample and gracious studio. Auntie Helen, as she strode up and down with lithe, cat-like movements, made it appear a cage. And despite the odour of incense, its smell was also like a zoo.

I had little chance to look around me until she retired to make tea in an alcove where a kettle was whistling on a Primus stove. I was aware only of an impression of sparse luxury, a desert of a room dotted with rich oases.

The central feature was a rough-hewn black beam a foot square which rose from the floor to the rafter-peak. Round it was twisted the skin of a monster python, the symbol of Isis.

The walls had been washed white, but the beams and the floor were black. There were a few rugs on the floor, diminutive in so large a room, but excellent in colour and design. They lay there, as though someone had dropped them, like gloves.

The smell of incense was rising from an elaborate and, as I found later, ponderous Chinese burner in the form of a dragon holding in the jaws of its uplifted head a chased bowl.

Against one wall was placed a huge divan which must by night have served her as a bed, but during the day was a couch of Arabian opulence, covered with a rich spread and heaped high with cushions of diverse designs which somehow achieved exotic harmony.

If I describe first the room, it is for the convenience of orderly narration. My observations were at the time distracted by the activities of the mongooses and the parrot.

When I entered the room, the mongooses retired for a period beneath the divan. But when the kettle started to whistle, they emerged again and renewed their stampede across the bare boards, skidding wildly at corners on the polished floor. As when I first visited a chicken-run, I thought that they were fighting each other, for lack perhaps of snakes, until I saw the hinder one catch the dainty fugitive beneath the elegant spinet and fiercely consummate the pursuit of love.

From a wire cage over by the window a grey parrot watched this scrabbling courtship testily, shifting from leg to leg as he worked himself into a frenzy, which when I approached burst from his throat in a torrent of rage. A half-blind pine-marten was chained to a beam.

Through the window in the twilight I could see a roof of Balliol and to the left the lights of the Cornmarket were beginning to creep into the sky. A couple of doors away was the Northgate Café, with the pretty waitresses who were going to marry undergraduates by hook or if necessary by crook, the hot plates of anchovy toast, the cream buns, the éclairs, the jumbles and rhum babas, the prattle of undergraduate conversation, eager, futile, but as strong as saplings forcing rocks up to get to sunlight.

Without looking round, I knew that Auntie Helen was standing behind me, looking at the city which despite its disappointments stood in my mind for beauty, freedom and the exultation of youth, and she was trembling.

"An evil city," she said in the voice of Phèdre, "a city full of hypocrites and Philistines and scheming tradesmen. If I wasn't a prisoner, don't imagine I should live here. I should be away . . . away!" The climax to which her voice rose would have been theatrical in another woman, but to her it was natural.

Her vibrant imagination reminded me of an anecdote, probably apocryphal, of one of the Dukes of Marl-

borough, who was observed standing on the terrace of
Blenheim Palace, shaking with ungovernable rage. When
asked what was the matter he pointed down the immense
avenue towards the gates, and there distantly could be seen
the figures of a young countryman and his wife, passing
the entrance of the Palace. "There they go!" he said,
"there they go! The Common People, God damn them!"

Yet, when I turned to her, she said in quite a different
voice, as if she was really Auntie Helen and I her nephew,
"I know how hungry young men get, so I've provided a
special tea for you!" And taking my hand, she led me to
the divan.

Her special was the routine tea of the Northgate, the
same brandysnaps, éclairs, cream horns and Australian
shortcake. But instead of Indian, Ceylon or China tea, she
served Earl Grey.

"Why do you think all tradesmen are scheming?" I
asked as I bit into a cream-filled brandysnap.

"They batten on other people," she said. "They grow
fat, while artists starve. If I had my way, I'd string them
up from every lamp-post."

The thought of dear Mr James Brown dangling from a
lamp-post, with his ultimate dew-drop frozen to his wine-
fine nose, filled me with sorrow. "But you couldn't do
that."

"I know," she answered, with a slyness which came
strangely from a tragedy queen, "but You Don't have to
Pay Their Bills."

This was the only time I ever heard her laugh. Even so,
I felt that it put me back where I started, outside the door
with the Moorish lamp unlit, perhaps the panel slid back.

"Even the Aristocrat today must trade," she said. "Trade on tradesmen! That's fair, isn't it?"

To set down what I discovered about Auntie Helen's life-story as I discovered it would be as wearisome to the reader as it was to me. Auntie Helen had no gift for consecutive narrative. She liked talking and her favourite subject was herself; but in her lonely attic life she had been so starved of human companionship that into our brief meetings she wanted to crowd the thoughts and observations of years. Reminiscence, imperfect recollections of the authors she admired—Nietzsche, Swinburne, Plato and Edward Carpenter—and her own motley beliefs came tumbling off her tongue higgledy-piggledy.

To build up a picture of her progress was like trying to write a biography from a collection of snapshots and volumes of press-cuttings, or to reproduce the skeleton of *Homo pithecanthropus* from two back teeth and a fragment of jawbone. Conjecture is an important ingredient of my narrative.

Helen was devoted to her father. He was a man of rare genius and spiritual insight, she said. She considered herself *his* child, not her mother's; and she resented her sex, because it was not like his.

But despite her admiration for her father's genius, the only example of it which she gave me was that when he was chief librarian of the Bodleian he removed crude notices such as Please Adjust your Dress before Leaving, and set in their place Greek couplets of his own composition conveying the same requests with far more wit and delicacy.

In the atmosphere of the University itself eccentricity when combined with scholarship flourishes like the green bay tree. But Auntie Helen grew up in North Oxford, where the climate is more rigorous. As she described her mother's week-end tea-parties and musical evenings, the endless parade of eligible but unenthusiastic undergraduates, and her sisters' tireless pursuit of matrimony, I was reminded of Samuel Butler's description in *The Way of All Flesh* of the storm which arose among the Allaby girls in such another North Oxford family, as to which of them should become Mrs Theobald Pontifex and their father's solution. "Wait till tomorrow, and then play at cards for him."

For the characters of *The Way of All Flesh* Butler drew on life. Even in my time Allabies, less crude but no less designing, still existed in North Oxford; and no doubt they will continue to exist as long as dons have daughters.

But Auntie Helen drew for her own character not on life but on literature. She was a heroine out of Ibsen, cousin to Hedda Gabler, Hilda Wangel and Nora Helmer. Normal human beings have a large repertory of personalities, from which they can select the rôle appropriate to the occasion. What gave Auntie Helen such dramatic force was the limitation of her character to a few simple modes of expression. As a character in a play she was perfectly conceived; but as a human being she was constricted almost to the point of insanity.

Yet when she talked of her girlhood she was more coherent, wider in her range, even in her way witty. Sitting with her in that dark attic illuminated 'for economy's sake' by two expensive candles which threw kind light across her anguished face, I caught in her voice the tones of the young girl she had been before I was born, phrases which she unearthed like the forgotten fragments at the bottom of an old trunk, a dance card, a silver slipper, a wildflower pressed between the leaves of a prayer book. They came out as fresh as new, and her face, the illusion maybe of the light, seemed smooth and young and even tender.

For a moment I caught a glimpse of her as she must have been before her nature and circumstance stretched her on the rack; a romantic rebel, an inflexible idealist, a passionate dreamer, who if she had met the right man might have found the love, happiness and beauty for which she hungered. No one could have given her a sense of humour, but a wise and tender man could have built a bridge between reality and her soul. Hers was the stuff of which great women are made.

Then the moment of lucidity was gone and we plunged back again into confusion. Husband-hunting among undergraduates had always been an arduous sport. Though her sisters pursued it with zest, Helen hated the thought of entangling those young men as much as they hated the thought of entanglement. North Oxford, which to some young girls was paradise, seemed to her a prison from which somehow she must escape to find the husband of her choice, her 'soul-mate' as she said.

Even in those days it was possible for a young lady, unhappy in her home-life, to find her freedom if she had determination enough. Helen could have trained for a job and moved to a place where she was more likely to find a suitable husband. But if she had, she would not have been Auntie Helen. Her mind worked differently.

She inserted an advertisement in a matrimonial paper and as a result she entered into correspondence with a Dutchman.

Once again, if she had not been Auntie Helen, she could easily have avoided bother, by having her pen-pal write to a mailing address. The fact that she didn't leads me to think that she wanted her family to know of the correspondence; that it was a gesture of revolt against North Oxford, intended to outrage her mother and sisters.

I could imagine the situation; the horror that any daughter of a Bodleian librarian should advertise for a soul-mate; what if the neighbours knew? The suspicion that the daughter who had always been so headstrong and difficult was barmy. The arguments:

"But Helen, don't you realise that no normal man would strike up an acquaintance with a girl through a matrimonial paper?" "But I'm bored to distraction by normal men. I want to meet an abnormal one." "But, my dear child, don't you realise that the sort of people who meet people through these papers are usually crooks or perverts?" "I put the advertisement in. Do you think I'm a crook or a pervert?" "You're just crazy!" "All right then. All I want is to find someone else as crazy as I am. Then I'll be happy."

How long they went on, the scenes, the tears and the recriminations, I don't know. Kind, sensible, exasperated, the family must have been utterly convinced of the rightness of their own judgement; the affair with the Dutchman could not go on. But I suspect that to Helen at this time revolt from the family was more important than any feelings she had towards her correspondent. North Oxford was not her world, and her insistence on her right to correspond with a world outside was the assertion of her independence. A prey to violent emotions which she hadn't the mental training to analyse, certain only that the way of life her family accepted was not hers, she fastened on the unknown Dutchman all her vague ambition. The more the family dissuaded her, the more determined not to yield she grew.

At last they began to threaten. The thought of the scandal, the laughter echoing through senior and junior common-rooms, may have decided them that if Helen was intent on self-destruction, their duty was to save the rest of the family. They told her that if she did not abandon the correspondence, she would have to leave the house. It was an ultimatum; and Helen behaved as most people of spirit do when faced with an ultimatum. She packed her bags and left the house at once.

The Dutchman, who was kept informed of every move in this domestic struggle, wrote begging her to come to Holland and marry him. But despite the stand which she had taken on his behalf against her family, she was not convinced that they were 'soul-mates.' She went instead to London, where she met Vickybird and 'that demon' Crowley.

"What time was this?" I asked her.

"It was in the summer of 1912," she said; "just before The Tragedy."

"What tragedy?"

"Vickybird had a friend, one of the most beautiful girls

77

I have ever seen. She died suddenly. If you never saw him before then, you never knew him at all. He's never recovered, really."

On this occasion she was too concerned with her own life-story to tell me more about 'The Tragedy,' and when I later tried to bring her back to it, she had thought better. "If he wants you to know," she said, "he will tell you himself."

It was through Vickybird that Auntie Helen became interested in the occult. She leapt at the chance of by-passing the slow, painful processes of thought by magic, of letting stars make decisions which she was too stupid to make for herself. She wrote and asked the Dutchman the exact time and date of his birth; and then she had his horoscope and hers cast in conjunction.

Comparison of the two swept all her doubts aside. She went straight to a Post Office, took a telegraph form on which she wrote WE ARE DESTINED FOR EACH OTHER HELEN and caught the next boat to Holland.

She and her family were both right about the Dutchman. He was crazy. He was a crook. He was a pervert. And for good measure, he was in the tertiary stage of a disease which he transmitted to her.

"How she stuck him as long as she did, I shall never know," Vickybird said. "But at last even she had to admit she was defeated."

Whether her family offered to receive her back into the fold, I cannot say. If they did, it was inevitable that she should refuse. They had been right in what they had prophesied about the Dutchman, which in itself was enough to make it impossible to forgive them. But she had been right in thinking that their world was not hers. They were in the hosts of the Philistines, while she belonged to the select company of Artists.

Unfortunately she had no artistic talent of any sort nor, what would have served as well, a private income. Hence her imprisonment in Oxford.

She had evolved the philosophy that it was the duty of Society to maintain her, because she was an Artist; and the main burden of that duty devolved upon her family.

If they had seen eye to eye with her, she would have been content to live quietly in Chelsea, Montparnasse, Capri or Greenwich Village. But as they did not recognise their responsibility, she was forced to live in Oxford. For the wild woman who contemptuously flouted all they stood for, they might have little use; but if she lived in Oxford they couldn't let her starve. And unless an occasional cheque was forthcoming, there was always the danger that one Sunday afternoon when the drawing-room was filled with guests the door might open and a tall figure in black velvet enter with her tawny hair bound in a python-skin and a half-blind pine-marten perched upon her shoulder, holding on a double leash a brace of mongooses straining towards the cakestand.

Yes, that was good for a quid a week.

I had tea many times with Auntie Helen, but seldom, after that first encounter, alone. The intensity of her manner and the incoherence of her conversation were embarrassing tête-à-tête. But what I found still more disquieting was her incandescent desire. While her behaviour and conversation were never indecorous, I could always feel the pulsation of her physical need, like the warm air rising from a well-insulated furnace, desperately in need of being stoked.

I have called her a handsome panther or leopardess; but she was more like Venus, not Anadyomene as Botticelli pictured her, just risen from the sea and riding ripe for love upon a scallop shell, but the ageing, rampant Venus of *Cupid and Psyche*, consuming herself with a desire so intense that it could never be satisfied, having clearly so much to offer that no one would sip for fear of surfeit.

Though unspoken and as I believe she thought carefully hidden by herself, this hunger was so patent that when alone with her I felt that I was guilty of a breach of manners in not flinging her back upon the exotic cushions and rendering her the service which the male mongoose rendered his mate so tirelessly beneath the spinet. Yet this was something from which I was restrained by the avidity of her craving.

So, to relax our tension, I introduced two friends of mine. Crispin Payne, the elder, had been at school with me. He looked more like Dorian Gray than anybody I have known, though he took looking like Dorian Gray less seriously than that unfortunate child of Wilde's æstheticism was allowed to. Beautifully dressed in a powder-blue suit which brought out the colour of his eyes, he would mount the stairs to Auntie Helen's, carrying on his forearm a black silk umbrella which had never been unrolled and in his hand a white Arum lily which he presented to Auntie Helen after kissing her tenderly upon the mouth.

In her infrequent salons, Auntie Helen liked to dominate the stage. But Crispin, who had a social ease remarkable in a young man of twenty, refused to accept her in the rôle of tragedy queen. He treated her like an indulgent uncle who though fond of her was not prepared to stand for girlish tantrums. Probably nobody, unless it were her father, had treated Auntie Helen in that way, and she was not sure whether she liked it. She was equally unsure whether she disliked it.

One afternoon while Colin Summerford was playing Bach at the spinet, Crispin leant back towards where she was sitting on the cushions, so that his golden head was close to Auntie Helen. With his lips, which were beautifully cut, invitingly parted, he looked up at her.

After a time she noticed him. She looked down into his eyes and then she turned to Colin.

Crispin lay quite still. His only movement was a slight flickering of the lips, as she turned once more to look at him. Then slowly she bent down and kissed him on the mouth.

When she had finished, he sat up again with a small smile on his face, while through her body passed a convulsive tremor.

"I like your friend Mr Summerford," said Auntie Helen later; "he has a beautiful aura. But Mr Payne. . . . I don't like to criticise your friends, but isn't he rather a playboy?"

We fixed our attention firmly on the comic aspects of Auntie Helen. As we went away, we would roar with laughter at her theosophical *bêtises*. She became a private joke between us, a conversational show-piece among others.

But secretly the three of us admired her grandeur and were awed by her tragic folly. She had a noble spirit, made absurd by ignorance, bitter by poverty, and eccentric by loneliness. With a private income of five thousand a year, she would have been a famous hostess.

These tea-parties brought ease to her spirit, provided a contact with the outside world which, though not fully satisfying, enabled her giddy brain to regain balance. But small as their cost was, they consumed the few shillings which she had in ready cash.

We invited her to meals. She refused. We brought supplies of cakes. She was insulted. "I'm old enough to be your mother," she said. "As if I can't afford to give a tea-party!"

But the bitter truth was, she couldn't; and in feeding her spirit (she began to talk about 'our little circle') we were starving her body. "We are all Artists," I said, "and these afternoons are so nice. But can't I give you some money, so that you won't have to stint yourself?"

"My dear boy," she said, "if I didn't know that you said this in kindness I would turn you out of my house. I don't want your money and I'll tell you why. As an Artist who will have to fight the Philistines all your life, the sooner you learn this the better. Remember: PROVIDED YOU ORDER THE BEST, THERE'S NO NEED TO PAY FOR IT."

"I don't understand," I said.

"Shopkeepers," she said, "are parasites on society. The important thing to know is that they are snobs. Never be mean. If you want a small bottle of eau-de-Cologne, you can't put it on the bill. Buy a pint of Chanel. Don't drink beer. Order champagne; by the dozen at least. We Artists are the aristocrats of the world. But we must behave like aristocrats."

"But when the bills come in, what do you do?"

"I threaten to transfer my custom. There's nothing like that for bringing a tradesman to heel."

"But in the end they must demand payment."

"When they really become offensive," she said, "you really do transfer your custom."

I was appalled. "What do you do when they sue you?" I asked.

"They don't," she said. "Not for amounts under fifty pounds. It used to be a hundred. Things are getting tighter. . . . I don't know what the world is coming to. . . . But any big store knows that if they sue someone who can't afford to pay a big bill, they'll drive away all the people who really can. That is an axiom of Credit, which is more important for Us than all the nonsense they teach you here of economics."

"But there are such people as debt collectors," I suggested.

"Debt collectors! Underpaid, snivelling, little bullies! No, it's the bailiffs that matter. They *can* be dangerous."

"All the same," I said, "your credit must constantly be shrinking. A time will come when you'll have to pay cash."

"Will it?" she asked. "I've been doing this for sixteen years and I've only just reached Edinburgh. I haven't touched Wales or Ireland yet. The trouble is bread and milk and things like that. They're so expensive these days."

This was Nietzsche in action, the philosophy of the over-man applied by the under-dog. It was a rôle so unlike any of Auntie Helen's others that I listened fascinated. It might even, I feared, be useful later on, because I had so far adopted the philosophy of the Sanctuary as to believe that nothing I wrote which was any good would bring me money.

"It's the bread and milk," I said, "that I'm thinking of. Wouldn't a pound . . .?"

"I don't want your money," she said, "but it is possible that you and your friends could help me sometime. If so, I'll call on you."

As I went down into Ship Street, I began to see the reason for things which had puzzled me—the iron grille, the sliding panel, the spyhole too small to poke a writ through quickly, the bolted door. I understood the Earl Grey tea, the expensive candles for economy's sake, the splendour and the sparseness.

When we had this conversation, Wall Street had just crashed. In the United States marginal speculators were tearing ticker-tape in their fists and leaping from the upper storeys of skyscrapers with a careless disregard for the bankrupts walking on the sidewalks below.

For a day or two the crash made banner headlines in the English Press. That businessmen should bump themselves off as casually as Al Capone's gang bumped off their rivals was news. The City Editors warned us that repercussions would be felt throughout Europe later. But comparatively few people felt an immediate pinch.

Auntie Helen was among the first. A creature of credit, she was a seismograph of financial disturbance. The days of the artistic outlaw were ended. The long holiday was over. Across the country, bailiffs like beaters started to move in and the Auntie Helens were the first to be flushed.

One noon the three of us found heather-coloured deckle-edged envelopes in our pigeon-holes. To us, now connoisseurs of that fantastic script, the handwriting would have betrayed agitation, even if in one corner had not been scrawled URGENT and in another IMPORTANT.

I opened mine and read:

> Dear Mr Calder-Marshall,
>
> Will you please visit me IMMEDIATELY you receive this note bringing with you your LARGEST suitcase (or Gladstone Bag).
>
> P.S. Pull the bell three times sharply.
>
> P.P.S. These Philistines shall not have My Lovely Things.

I pulled the bell three times sharply and the panel immediately shot back. She had been waiting on the other side and the door was open in a flash. To hell with mysticism! Bugger the stars! The swag was laid out all ready.

She tore open the suitcase and piled in first the incense-burner and then the heavy candle-sticks. I saw her rings sparkle in the light.

"What about your rings?"

She snapped the case to and held her hands up. "Glass," she said. "Coloured glass, not worth tuppence.

I never had a bit of jewelry worth a thing. Except one, and I pawned that and lived on it for three months."

I lifted the suitcase. It was so heavy it seemed to pull my arm out of its socket. "What do you want me to do with this?" I asked. "Just keep it," she answered, bundling me towards the door. "This may never have happened before in your life, but it has happened many times in mine. It's like measles. It lasts about three weeks and then they go away."

"I'm sorry, Auntie Helen," I said, turning at the door; "it's horrible to think of this happening to you."

She saw my doleful face and took my chin in her hand and shook it. "My boy," she said, "if nothing worse than this ever happens to you, you'll be a very happy man." She closed the door and then she opened it again. "The siege is now ON," she said, grinning.

As I humped that ponderous case towards my college I felt cheated, even, I confess, a little jealous. I had thought vainly that Crispin, Colin and I had brought some relief into her monotonously lonely life. Now I saw that we were pawns in the game that she was playing against the filthy Philistines.

In her fantasy she may have been replaying the game she had lost against the family in North Oxford. I do not know. All I am sure of is that she welcomed the bailiffs. She wanted conflict and she wanted a man in the house.

Perhaps the bailiffs provided both. But I don't think so. Before they came, she was as eager as a bride. When they left and I brought back the swag, she was sadder than a woman who had been deprived of satisfaction.

I set up the Chinese incense-burner on its table. To do

so I had to shift some papers to the side, circulars from the large stores in Belfast.

"Come and see me soon. Bring Mr Payne and Mr Summerford," she said as I left. "And it'll be like old times."

"Yes, we must do that," I answered; "they were good, weren't they?" But I felt a resentment against her, because she had already given a past to me, who wanted only the future. All the same, I took her hand and on an impulse bent my head and kissed it, feeling against my chin the enormous property glass rings which even bailiffs didn't think worth while taking.

I wanted to see Auntie Helen again soon, not because it would be like the old times which had become boring, but because it would certainly be different. The idea of a transcendental crook intrigues me, even now. And I hold it against the Senior Proctor of that time that he summoned me next day to his presence.

I went, full of guilty suspicions, none of which was connected with poor old Auntie.

"Mr Calder-Marshall?"

"Sir?"

"I understand you have been visiting the apartment of a Mrs Helen —— in Ship Street."

"Certainly, sir. She is an old friend of mine."

"I must instruct you not to visit there again or to see the lady."

"Isn't that equally insulting, sir, to the lady and to me?"

"It is insulting to nobody, Mr Calder-Marshall. This is merely a notification from the University Authorities, who if what you say is correct are better informed than you are, that in their opinion the lady in question is not suitable to consort with undergraduates."

"She's so pathetic," I said. "What would happen, sir, if I went to tell her of your decision?"

"That, Mr Calder-Marshall, is a question the answer to which you would be given, only if you were foolish enough to do so."

I walked out furious with the Senior Proctor, furious partly because it seemed that the battalions of North Oxford still commanded the treatment of this pathetic woman, but, I admit, far more furious that the Proctor shouldn't understand that the last thing I wanted was to become her lover.

About a year later, when I came back from a holiday in France, Vickybird said, "You remember how Auntie Helen always wanted to escape from Oxford. Well, while you were away she did escape. She had enough money to get from Oxford to Worthing and then the bus fare out to Cissbury. The bailiffs were in her place and she couldn't smuggle anything out. She pretended that she was taking the mongooses for a walk. And the bailiffs were only too pleased to get rid of *them*. They liked biting bailiffs.

"She hadn't eaten for days, apparently, but when she ran out of money at Cissbury, she began to walk to the Sanctuary with the mongooses in a basket, and she walked until she fainted.

"Then a motorist picked her up and took her to the Sanctuary. And there she stayed until she died."

"What did she die of?"

"It's a curious thing," said Vickybird; "you mustn't tell this to Kathleen. But when Auntie Helen first came to London, I was living with a girl of quite outstanding beauty, and when she met Auntie Helen, she said to her, 'You will die of Venus.' And so she did. Auntie Helen died of General Paralysis of the Insane."

Part Two

THE ABBEY OF THELEMA

Chapter Four

Two Large Elephants

*

MY father was possessed of a restless spirit which took him abroad for years at a time and sent his family posting from one furnished house to another. He was, he was fond of saying, a modern Ishmael; and in the fifteen years of my life before he bought my grandfather's house at Steyning, we had lived in eleven different houses. It was an interesting experience, because the home life of our landlords, revealed by diaries, letters and even account-books, provided us with vicarious enjoyments denied to children in more settled homes.

My father's decision to buy his own house marked a new phase in his development. The time had come to settle down. But his choice of Steyning was unfortunate, because his business and my school were in London; and the seclusion which made it a heaven for week-ends and holidays made it hell for week-days.

Hitherto we had hovered on the frontiers of suburbia, moving gradually further out as each new compromise between the town and country became engulfed by the speculative builders. But now that we had a truly rural home, my father decided we should have a truly urban flat in Central London.

He found the very thing in a block of red brick flats overlooking the backside of Bedford Square. From my window I could watch Lady Oxford's butler dressing, and sometimes undressing.

Just as at Steyning I had never lived so deep in the country, so in Bloomsbury I had never lived so close to the heart of a great city. Before I went to bed, I would turn out the lights in my bedroom, open the window and listen to the distant roar of traffic down Tottenham Court Road.

Tottenham Court Road was sooty, strident and unimpressive in daytime. I preferred the quiet elegance of Bedford Square, the noble expanse of Lincoln's Inn Fields, the delitescency of Red Lion Passage or the Oriental bookshops by the British Museum with their latent mystery as if they were the beginning of a story by Algernon Blackwood.

But as night fell, London changed. I believed at the age of fifteen in Life with a capital as unquestioningly as in God, Love, Art and Lust. As the sun sank and the illuminations of shop-windows rose, Life came into Tottenham Court Road like lions from their cages roaring. Then was never a place so brilliant in my fancy as St Giles's Circus, where on the site of what is now the Dominion Cinema was a perennial Fun Fair, a miniature Luna Park, with a deafening competition of barkers, steam-organs and dodgem cars to assail the ears, and to engross the eyes girls in the search of pleasure whose frail features and experimental make-up were well-treated by the yellow lights.

When I craned forward from my window, I could see like an endless pageant through the blazing street red buses with their anonymous cargoes of humanity, individually intent on pleasure, crime or business, but from afar like dominoes in a nightly masquerade. And yet the street in which we lived was, for the most part, as quiet as a country lane, being frequented at this hour by lap- and house-dogs taking their masters or their servants for an airing before putting them to bed. These silent men, like prisoners so long incarcerated that even the brief period of exercise no longer gave them pleasure, stood chained to their animals under street-lamps or at the base of plane trees, glancing listlessly once or twice at the car- nival roistering past the far end of the street, but as if it was a world from which they were forever separated; at the least tug of the leash they would move eagerly on in the direction of their cells.

As they were of their pets, I felt the prisoner of my im- maturity. But for me there was hope of release. Some day, the sooner the better, I should join that splendid cavalcade.

It was distance that lent enchantment to Tottenham Court Road at night, allowing me to make it an image of adult delight. When I came closer to the reality, I liked it less.

Today the Horseshoe is a model of respectability, a very proper pub for Masons to banquet in. But even in the thirties, when it was made over and the saloon bar laid open to the street with great plate-glass windows which could be raised in hot weather, there was an element of doubt about its reputation. "I can't make out," I heard a woman say to her friend, "whether that place is Frenchy or Just Low."

But in 1923 there was no doubt. It was Low.

Every night when it closed, bleary drunks reeled and staggered across the pavement, while cheery drunks sang, shouted and brandished bottles in the air. As the contents of the bars were emptied like barrels of live fish into the street, fights broke out, intermittent but savage eruptions of drunken rancour which embroiled onlookers and even passers-by.

One night I saw two women quarrelling. They wore hats bedecked with feathers and fastened with long steel hatpins. They screamed abuse at one another, and when they could scream no louder, both suddenly fell silent and started to remove their hatpins. This was done by tacit consent, rather in the way that in a bullfight the *suerte de picar* gives place to the *suerte de banderillear*. They placed their hats on the pavement, jabbed in the hatpins and set about one another in earnest. There was nothing barred. Kicking, scratching, biting and shrieking, they tore at each other's hair and faces with an unlovely passion that outraged my carefully nurtured concepts of the Gentle Sex.

Yet, scandalised though I was and disgusted, I fought to keep my place amongst the bystanders; because this, though in the raw, was Life.

Within the ring of spectators the women fought with self-absorption. There might have been no one within miles for all the notice they took. But when at last a large man, as burly as a policeman and as fumblingly officious, tried to separate them with an "'Ere, 'ere, you can't do that, yer know!" they instantly stopped fighting one another and rounded on him for not minding his own business with a torrent of abuse that amounted almost to physical violence.

As he reeled back amazed, they picked up their hats, pinned them on their heads and walked off arm in arm.

I had never seen among adults a quarrel so unbridled nor one so quickly mended. The climate of my life had been temperate. Perhaps that was why I was attracted by the violent expression of emotion. Many children brought up in the atmosphere of immoderation long for restraint at any price. But for me the road of excess led to the palace of wisdom and any experience was better than none.

Bloomsbury and Soho were territories as fertile in experience as the high Andean jungle to William Beebe, as fertile and almost as primitive. I thought this was as true for my brother as myself. But I was not certain, because a chasm had yawned between us.

My brother had left school and as a freshman was eagerly clambering up the foothills of manhood. As a schoolboy four years his junior, I had become an encumbrance, an unpleasant reminder of how recent were his own schooldays. The more desperately I tagged behind him, the more eager he was to shake me off.

There may be joys peculiar to the age of fifteen, but in this incarnation I missed them. I wanted to burn up the years until I left school; by some magic to become my brother's coeval.

This ambition drove me into absurd predicaments, as I steeled myself to acquire tastes for which I was not ripe. As an undergraduate, my brother was permitted to drink beer at home. Immediately I advanced my own claims for beer, arguing that David Copperfield had drunk porter at the age of ten.

"If you like beer," said my father, "of course you can have beer." So every evening by my place was set a bottle of Fremlin's Elephant Ale.

The trouble was, I didn't like beer. Its smell was repulsive and its tang made me wince. But to drink beer was a proof of manhood, and it was not long before I had schooled myself to drink a whole pint of the unpalatable stuff without betraying my disgust.

Fremlin's Elephant Ale was usually delivered by the crate from the Off Licence in Great Russell Street. Finding that she had forgotten to renew the supply, one evening my mother asked my brother to go to the Off Licence to buy some more. "Why can't Arthur get it?" asked my brother, without looking up from the copy of D. H. Lawrence's *Birds, Beasts and Flowers* that he was reading on the sofa.

It was his usual answer at this time, and my reply was usually, "Why, just because I'm the younger, do I have to do everything beastly?" But in this case I took the money, fetched a basket and went out. I knew if I protested my brother would say, "He's only fifteen, of course. Under the legal age. They wouldn't give it to *him*."

"If they do give it to me," I thought, "then it'll show I *look* older anyway."

When I reached the Off Licence it was shut. All the shops were shut. It was early-closing day. In a way I was glad, because I should not have to risk a snub.

Then across Tottenham Court Road I saw the lights of

the Blue Posts. "Why on earth didn't you go to a pub, then?" my brother would say if I went back. "I suppose you funked it."

Very slowly I walked down Great Russell Street and across Tottenham Court Road into Hanway Place, where was the entrance to the saloon bar. Someone went in. Inside looked smoky and crowded. Someone came out. No one was singing or fighting. It was better to be snubbed by a stranger than laughed at by a brother. I pushed open the door.

Behind the bar was a peroxide blonde who pulled beer dreamily as she conversed with a red foxy-faced man sitting on a stool. Her cheeks were white with powder, her thin lips painted with greasy lipstick in a parody of passion. From home training I knew she was 'common' and probably 'fast.' She appeared entrancingly desirable, even though she was pathetically plain and undernourished. I liked standing there not being served. It was a cheap peek at Life.

Having served customers to my right and left, she deigned to notice me. "And what do you want, son?" she asked.

The 'son' riled me (though it might have been 'sonny'). In a loud, clear voice which betrayed the timidity it was meant to disguise, I said, "I want two large Elephants, please!" This sentence, formulated as I hesitated outside, seemed to me a triumph of *expertise*, until I saw the expression on the girl's face.

"I'm sorry, son," she said; "I didn't quite catch."

"A couple of large Elephants," I repeated, laying my money on the counter. "Or four small ones would do."

She turned to a managerial person by her side. "There's a young gentleman here," she said in a ringing voice, "wanting to buy elephants. Could you see to him?"

The bar was silent. The customers knew they were on to a good thing. The Manager asked me to repeat my request. I did so with what I hoped was the proper scorn of anybody in the pub business who didn't know what an Elephant was. "There's a pet shop up the road, son," he said, "but I doubt they could give you delivery tonight."

This and the roar of laughter which followed it made me realise the *double entendre*, but I was too ashamed to laugh myself. "Don't you," I asked with surging contempt, "don't you keep Fremlin's Elephant Ale?"

"Oh," said the barmaid. "This is a Hoare's house, sonny, not a Fremlin's. What about two large Hoares?"

Nearly capsized in the hurricane of laughter which this suggestion raised, I paid across my money, snatched the large Hoares and pushed into the street.

But I didn't go straight home. There are moments, especially in adolescence, when Life stacks the cards against one and Art must be called on for a re-deal. I had after all been rather courageous in getting this beer, but to secure the recognition for my bravery I knew that a slight rearrangement of inessential detail was needed. I walked round Bedford Square several times before it came out right.

There was a clink of bottles as I got into the lift. "That sounds like a bit of the right stuff," said the porter.

I rattled the nauseous quarts deliberately. "Nothing like a drop of beer," I lied.

My brother was still lying on the sofa reading D. H.

Lawrence. "You've been a long time," he said, without looking up.

I told him what had happened, omitting any description of my state of mind. It was not the whole truth, but it was nothing but the truth until the end. " 'This is a Hoare's house,' she said, 'not a Fremlin's.' So I said, 'All right, miss, I'd like two large Hoares.' And they all laughed. And then she gave me the change, which was tuppence cheaper than Fremlin's. So I said, 'Thank you, miss. Hoares are cheaper in the Tottenham Court Road than Elephants are in Great Russell Street.' "

The next day my mother told me that my brother thought I was less 'earnest' than I used to be.

The penitential quiet of our street was broken on most nights between nine forty-five and ten fifteen. There were high voices, laughter, shouting and sometimes a rather nice voice singing *The Raggle-Taggle Gypsies*.

As I sat at my desk trying to compose Greek or Latin verse, I would look up and curse. "Those filthy drunks again!" I'd say. Then I would turn out my light and open the window and look down on them with an envy I called contempt. I watched them go down the street, the unimaginably beautiful girls and the fantastically gay young men, and I said, 'Thank God I am not like that.'

"Hypocrisy is the homage which Vice pays to Virtue," I had marked in my la Rochefoucauld. But in my heart I knew that hypocrisy was an adolescent substitute for sin.

I watched them down the street and even listened till their voices were sunk in the hum of London. Then, closing the window, I went back to the ignorant imitation in foreign tongues of verse that ancient poets had written from experience in their own.

"What's the rabble," I asked my brother, "that goes down the street night after night about ten o'clock?"

"When you grow up," he answered, "you will find that in certain parts of London there is a tidal flow from pubs. The Fitzroy Tavern, which is north of Oxford Street and west of Totters, closes at ten. At that time, those who wish to go on drinking either flow south to Soho or east to Bloomsbury. We are on the direct route to the Plough."

"It's disgusting. I was looking out of my window last night . . ."

"If you think it's disgusting, why do you look out of your window?" he asked. "Don't do it. You might see me."

A few nights later I did see him. "Bobby!" I shouted, "Bobby!"

He looked up, and I saw his white face among his friends.

"Bobby!" I yelled.

He went on down the street and round the corner.

If he had stopped, I would have run down the stairs and been with him in a moment, and to hang with the *Medea* or *Œdipus Tyrannus*.

The next morning he wasn't looking very well. "Why didn't you stop last night?" I asked.

"What *are* you talking about?"

"You know."

"I don't. And I'd advise you not to, either."

"Arthur is an intellectual," remarked my brother one day, allowing just sufficient time for me to swell with pride before he added, "I, of course, am an æsthete."

There was nothing for it but to discover what an æsthete was and then become one. "Æstheticism," prompted the dictionary, "a proneness to indulge and cultivate the sense of the beautiful."

Though not, if my brother was right, prone to indulge, I could at least cultivate the sense of the beautiful; and this I did, at first dutifully and then with avidity, at art galleries, exhibitions and museums.

The most convenient, and so my favourite, source of culture was the British Museum, where among the pitch-black mummies and rude statues of the god Men, I discovered the young Queen Nefertiti. I fell in love with the balance of her forward-thrusting neck, the uplifted chin and the superb line of her profile extended by the head-dress. Here was the reassurance that Art could transcend Life; not merely in the common sense that centuries after the woman who sat had lost her beauty and the man who made, his skill; while the object of their collaboration was as lovely as the day it was finished: but in the rarer sense that the unmoving model, with eyes like gems, lips that could never part and a head that did not turn, was so perfect that sight, speech or movement could have done nothing but detract from her beauty.

My brother, I discovered, had never heard of Queen Nefertiti; so on his next vacation I took him round to see her. He was enthralled by her as I was, but as we moved away I sensed that he was angry. His was the rôle of pioneer, mine of camp-follower. He resented their reversal and I knew that he would redress the balance as soon as possible.

As we left the Museum gardens there burst from a hotel almost opposite a woman followed by five men. "Taxi!" she shouted imperiously, "taxi!", first at a private car and then at a cab with the flag down.

She was conspicuously dressed in a coat of tigerskin and a cap to match. With breeches, top-boots and a whip I could have fancied her putting a troupe of large cats through their routine, so masterful was her manner. Yet as she stood at the head of her échelon of retainers, there was nothing unwomanly about her. Domination was not the denial of her sex but its prerogative.

Her coat was not done up, and though it was not possible to see exactly what she was wearing beneath it, a medley of bright colours was revealed so startling in contrast that it seemed impossible that they could harmonise; and yet, with a flair for colour like a Romany, she had so arranged them that they were brilliantly effective. Her beauty, too, was like a gypsy's, her unpainted face achieving beauty by the clear curve of the jaw, the arching nostrils, the high broad cheekbones and the sharp, catlike eyes.

She was not young by my standards, at least thirty-five; yet age was not a thing which entered my mind. Even into the summoning of a taxi she put an energy that made the men behind her look like dummies.

They were a queer party; four of them young, with bright tussore ties, coloured shirts and flannel trousers, the uniform of Oxford and Cambridge; the fifth an older man, looking the worse for wear.

As a taxi stopped and the woman got in followed by the four young men, there was an argument as to where they should go, and no one paid any attention to the tatty man, who as he stood slightly dazed and dusty on the pavement looked as if he had been knocked down in a street-fight and suffered slight concussion of the brain.

"Come on," they called from the inside of the cab, "there's plenty of room."

"Ah don't mind payin' for you, Betty," the man said slowly, "but ah'm not made of brass and ah'm damned if ah'll go on standin' treat for these young fellers any longer." His face had turned very red and his fists were clenched.

"Why on earth don't you go back to Huddersfield, then, like you've been promising for the last week?" said the woman. "If you think I tolerate my friends being insulted by a man who makes fancy woollen goods, you're mistaken." She slammed the door. "Sordid little man!"

As the taxi-driver leaned back to take his instructions, the man from Huddersfield poked his head through the window. "'Uddersfield," he shouted, "aye, that's where ah'm goin', and yer won't catch me comin' to London again in an 'urry. Not ruddy laikely, yer won't."

The starting taxi wrenched the door from his grasp but it did not stop the stream of homely northern invective with which he speeded the parting cab. "Ah've learned my lesson," he kept saying; but to judge from his face, across which fatigue and drunkenness, anger and desire chased and collided like dodgem cars, he had not yet got it by heart.

He spat into the gutter as the taxi turned out of sight.

Then he removed his hat, brushed it perfunctorily with his sleeve, replaced it on the centre of his balding pate and aimed himself at the door of the hotel from which he had come.

"Well! Well! Well!" said my brother. "What do you make of that?"

"That marvellous-looking woman!" I said. "I suppose she's somebody awfully famous, like an actress."

"That was Betty May, the Epstein model," my brother said, "the woman who married Raoul Loveday, who was ritually murdered by Crowley in the Abbey of Thelema at Cefalu."

"How do you know?" I asked, jealous.

"She's often in the Fitzroy Tavern," he answered; "I saw her there last night."

The triumph of Queen Nefertiti was short-lived. A live Epstein model, I had to admit, trumped any dead Queen of Egypt.

Chapter Five

The Adonis of Cefalu

*

MY brother maintained till the day he died that Raoul Loveday was ritually murdered by The Beast in the Abbey of Thelema at Cefalu. Sometimes he would say that Crowley at Evening Pentagram severed Loveday's jugular vein and the members of the order drank his blood; at others he preferred the theory that, like the straw effigies of Adonis, his body was flung into the sea.

This was strange, because though the precise nature of what Loveday was doing in the Abbey was obscure and his motives for going to Cefalu debatable, the one thing of which there was no doubt was that Loveday died what any doctor would certify as a natural death, and my brother should have known this.

He was able to deny Betty May's story that Loveday died from some sort of enteric fever, on the grounds that if she had told the true story, The Beast would have sued for criminal libel. But what struck me as strange was that he cited, as the irrefutable evidence of ritual murder, the investigation made by a friend of Loveday's, a medical student, shortly after the death.

This friend, or it would be better to say acquaintance, was really more interested in The Beast than in Loveday himself; and this was probably true of my brother and many others beside him, to whom Loveday was merely the victim of a figure of inhuman evil. The medical student fancied himself a latter-day St George, setting out intrepidly to attack The Beast in his lair, with as his weapon only the general knowledge of a doctor about to qualify.

The Beast was not in his lair at the time, and the notorious Abbey proved to be a pleasant, if insanitary, farmhouse in the grounds of which was playing as healthy a bunch of children as you could find in any Montessori School. The only clue to ritualistic orgies lay in The Beast's sanctum, *La Chambre des Cauchemars*, which was embellished by perverse erotic paintings and the reproduction of a tripod found at Herculaneum, each leg of which was an ithyphallic satyr.

When he was interviewed, the local doctor who had attended Loveday, too late perhaps but at the end, swore that his death was due to natural causes, "a grippe that went to the lungs." Since the doctor was also the Mayor of Cefalu and the local fascist boss, who was waiting for the earliest opportunity to expel Crowley from Sicily, there was every reason to believe the truth of his verdict. The medical student returned to London, very reluctantly convinced of The Beast's innocence.

This was the man my brother cited to me as proof of the ritual murder!

I can only think that my brother never heard the story from him at first hand; but, like a message which is passed from mouth to mouth, the story had been twisted to mean the opposite.

The reasons why undergraduates wanted to believe that Crowley was a ritual murderer were probably complicated. The scientific rationalists had been hammering away for years at the basis of Christianity. They had destroyed the appetite for the Christian religion, without satisfying the hunger for faith. Sir James Frazer's theory that religion had deposed magic, and been deposed by science, which in its turn might be superseded by something not yet dreamed of, was intellectually exhilarating; but it did not take into account the craving which as undergraduates we had for the irrational. We might pooh-pooh the idea of a personal Satan, but given the chance of locating the Devil Incarnate in Cefalu we were not going to surrender it without a struggle. Loveday was of subsidiary interest; the victim in a fairy story, whose only function was to establish the wickedness of the ogre.

The story of Loveday never reached a simple, classic form, like the tale of Vickybird's metamorphosis, which was invariable except that there was some doubt as to which animal he had become. A dromedary or camel were the commonest forms, but my brother and I rejected them in favour of the zebra, on the grounds that as a zebra he stood a far better chance of getting into Alexandria Zoo. The popular version of Loveday was very scrappy. There was a story of his climbing in to college with a girl and being caught on two spikes and the girl going away and leaving him; a hint of orgies; and then the death. The rest was left to the imagination of the teller.

Disappointed in my brother's ritual sacrifice, I evolved a far more complex account of the whole affair, which I advance, not because I believe now that it is the correct explanation of what happened, but because it shows the length to which my undergraduate imagination was prepared to go in order to defend the sinister character of The Beast.

Loveday, when he was a scholar of St John's College, Oxford, was a stocky, untidy, carelessly dressed young man. Beneath his short hair, which was cut *en brosse*, he had a merry rather than a good-looking face, with bright blue eyes of incredible innocence.

He was a good soccer player and a spectacular climber. After the college gates were closed at midnight, he regularly climbed in and out. His feat of climbing the Martyrs' Memorial and cementing an enamel chamber-pot to the top won him a romantic fame throughout the university.

And to be a romantic figure was what he wanted more than anything else at this time. He took reality as a canvas on which to paint his dreams, a dressmaker's stand on which he modelled his fancy. He conveyed to one of his contemporaries that his father was a retired naval officer working in the Admiralty, to another that he was a Courier or King's Messenger. He was actually a retired petty officer, who was employed in the Admiralty carrying files from office to office.

Loveday's mind was preoccupied with girls, and the younger they were the better. He was astonishingly successful with them, partly perhaps because he had no doubt what he wanted from them, but also because his romantic manner made seduction 'sort of different.' He could call a waitress from the Kardomah 'my wine-dark rose,' and sound as if he meant it; probably because he did. His friends watched him with envy and some amusement chasing girls half his days and being chased by their parents and elder brothers half the night.

His poetry was as wildly romantic as his love-making. He admired immensely decadents like Dowson and Lionel Johnson who hid the petty in grandiloquence, bridging the gulf between reality and splendour with alcohol. He drank whisky by the toothglass.

That he should study mediæval magic, his friends considered part of the romantic picture. It made him interesting, different, and was even helpful in some erotic situations. Though he was never observed to do any work, he got a First in History quite literally by magic, owing to the brilliance and erudition of his answer to a question on the rôle of magic in mediæval society.

Up to this point, Loveday appeared to be an exceptionally typical undergraduate, in that he wrote in majuscule what his fellows scribbled in lower case. Just another romantic exhibitionist was all he seemed to be.

The reason for this was that at Oxford the strongest character is the University itself. It is like a hothouse. You put a number of young men in it and what you observe is merely the speed and luxuriance of growth in what appears to be a small number of different basic types. It is only after the young men have left Oxford and gone into the open world that their personal characteristics begin to emerge.

Loveday's individuality started to show itself even before he left Oxford. The pursuer of young shop-girls fell in love with Betty May, at least a dozen years older than himself, and married her.

They first met in the Harlequin Club in Beak Street,

and Loveday's friends in fun had built him up to Betty as a woman-hater.

"So you don't like women?" she asked.

"All Antony's love for Cleopatra was nothing to my love for you," he answered. It was a gambit which had often stood him in good stead, and it did so once again. Betty May thought he was wonderful; the way he took her in evening dress through Red Lion Square during a thunderstorm. "Revel in wetness!" he cried, and feeling his starched collar limp around his neck. "It's just like velvet!"

When he proposed to her, it was with his character-istic violence. "I shall kill myself and I shall kill you, too, if you don't marry me!"

It was difficult to assess exactly how much Loveday changed at this time. For his time at Oxford I had to rely on what his contemporaries said; and their prejudice was to regard him as not so very different from themselves. For his marriage and what happened later in Cefalu, my only source was Betty May's account.*

Apart from the constraint caused by the fear of libel, Betty May's story was written as an account of *her* life, not of Loveday's, and it obviously needed correction in order to arrive at what was happening to Loveday himself.

The chief change that was taking place in Raoul Love-day, I concluded, was that from being an undergraduate he was becoming a man. The girls that he chased at Ox-ford he invested with a romance they could not wear. Betty May was a person as romantic as himself, and far

* *Tiger Woman, My Story*, Betty May, Duckworth, 1929.

more experienced. She had done the sort of things which he wanted to do.

But there were two grave differences between them, one of education and the other of temperament. He was an intellectual, she an intuitive; she did what she wanted without a *mystique*, he needed the rationale of Do what thou Wilt shall be the whole of the Law. She was happy provided that her emotions were satisfied, but he had also a hungry intellect.

Temperamentally Betty May loved, or perhaps it would be truer still to say lusted after, life. The idea of suicide was foreign to her. To no imaginable situation could it prove the way out. Loveday was more than half in love with death. There is many a truth spoken in flirtation. "The love of Antony for Cleopatra" unconsciously revealed a desire for suicide as a result of frustrated love, and the terms of his proposal betrayed an equally self-destructive fantasy.

Even at Oxford, Loveday had conceived an enormous interest in and admiration for Crowley. He would anyway have sought him out when he came to London; but with better intellectual equipment Betty May could have parried or side-tracked the influence of The Beast. As it was, she played right into his hands.

During the war she had become a drug-addict and had been cured only after a struggle which demanded every ounce of character she possessed. Yet in talking to Loveday about her experience she probably fired him with the desire to take drugs at the very moment that she thought she was warning him against them. She stimulated an appetite which was the last she was prepared to satisfy but the first that Crowley chose to pander to.

When Loveday's chance came one night to meet Crowley, Betty May refused to go with him. He was away for two days and three nights, returning home on the third night by means of the rain-pipe running down the face of the house in Beak Street, where they lived on the third floor. Betty was woken by a scrabbling at the window-pane and switched on the light. His white face, smeared with soot, was caught in the light as he hung thirty feet above the pavement. Betty May flung open the window and dragged him to safety. He reeked of ether, and the moment she got him undressed and into bed he fell asleep.

When he came round, he swore that he would never see Crowley again. But as soon as the hangover was passed he was back with The Beast the moment that Betty May went out to a studio to pose.

The answer of most people when offered 'This or That' is instinctively to say 'Both.' He wanted to keep his Oxford friends, he wanted to keep Betty May, and he wanted The Beast. This was the only explanation of the conflicting stories and the contradictory conduct. He hid with Betty from The Beast at a new address and for a time Betty May felt triumphantly secure.

Then one evening there was a knock at the door and she opened it to a large man, wearing a Highland kilt. In his right hand the kilted figure bore a long wand round which was coiled a green snake; with this he described in the air the sign of the pentagram as he uttered the words, "Do what thou Wilt shall be the whole of the Law," in a solemn if Cockney voice.

From behind her came the voice of Loveday, "Love is the Law, Love under Will."

The Beast raised Betty May's hand to his lips, kissed it and then, fumbling in his sporran, produced a bottle of hock. "I've come to dinner," he said.

Betty May looked at her husband in astonishment; but he showed no surprise, probably because it was he who had arranged the visit.

She picked up her hat and coat. "I shan't cook a meal for you," she said, going furiously towards the door.

The Beast smiled. "The day will come," he said, "when you will cook all my meals for me."

Loveday's friends got the impression that he was aware of the dangers of associating with Crowley. Though The Beast's two previous secretaries had died mysteriously, Loveday said he considered himself safe because he hadn't any money. He gave Betty May the impression that he went to Crowley for an intellectual companionship he couldn't get from her. Yet when Crowley appeared, once again in Highland outfit * in a nightclub, and raising his wand announced to the general merriment, "Do what thou Wilt shall be the whole of the Law," Loveday solemnly stood up and answered, "Love is the Law, Love under Will." When loyalties were in conflict, loyalty to Crowley was transcendant.

As I understood it, during the period that Loveday spent with Crowley in London he was being initiated in

* This Highland outfit was, like the wand, copied from Mac-gregor Mathers, who in old age added a fanatic Jacobitism to his pursuit of magic and his delusion of military grandeur.

four different ways. He was instructed in general magic, having the run of Crowley's rare library. He was encouraged to take different drugs, ostensibly for the induction of trance-states, but even more importantly to create a physical dependence on his Master. He learned the rituals of The Beast's Temple and became familiar with the significance of different evocations. These on occasion had orgiastic elements which appealed to the strong streak of sensuality in Loveday. And finally he was being prepared for the Abbey of Thelema at Cefalu.

By the time that Crowley left for Sicily he had not the slightest fear that when he summoned Loveday he would come to him, and I believe also that Loveday knew that when he entered the Abbey he would cease to be Loveday and become Adonis.

I never made up my mind whether The Beast wanted Betty May to come with Loveday or not. I suspected that he did not care very much either way, but that as a man he preferred that she should come. She was a beautiful woman and she hated him. That was a double change from the rather plain women who adored him. In London he had taken her into a bedroom and told her to kneel at his feet and she had laughed at him. She would find it harder to laugh in the Abbey of Thelema, where the will of The Beast was supreme.

But nobody tried to persuade her to go to Sicily. She was invited, but Loveday didn't ask her to accept the invitation. He merely said that he was going anyway. On the way there, in Palermo, while they were waiting for the train to Cefalu, she ran away, furious that Raoul had sold her wedding ring to pay for their tickets on the last lap.

Loveday made no attempt to go after her. When she returned later, having failed to find the British Consul, she found him sitting on the table of the waiting-room, swinging his legs. "Hullo!" he said.

Betty May had no knowledge of or interest in magic, but even her account of what happened after that seemed to me strange. They arrived at Cefalu railway station at nine o'clock at night. She spoke no Italian and Loveday's was elementary. Yet there was no one from the Abbey to meet them.

They went up to the first Sicilian they saw and asked the way in broken Italian.

Speaking English in an American accent, the man said, "You want to go to the High Priest?"

"Damn the High Priest!" Betty May said. "We want Aleister Crowley."

"He is the High Priest," the man answered. "I am going that way and I will take you to the Abbey."

On the way to the Abbey, their guide met several people to whom he spoke in Italian, and these people turned and went with them to the Abbey, till by the time they arrived it was almost like a procession, said Betty May.

When I read this it seemed as strange to me as it had to her, until it occurred to me that perhaps it *was* a procession, and that when the man who spoke English said that Crowley was the High Priest, he really meant that to him he was the High Priest.

Loveday knocked on the door of the Abbey and it was flung back and The Beast, standing forth in his full vestments and describing in the air the sign of a pentagram with his wand, said, "Do what thou Wilt shall be the whole of the Law."

"Love is the Law," answered Loveday, "Love under Will." Then he stepped forward into the Abbey. But Betty May said nothing and the door was slammed and bolted in her face.

Immediately she was surrounded by the peasants who had followed. They began talking and trying to drag her away, with, she imagined, the basest of motives. What struck me as extraordinary was that they were not surprised and, as good Catholics, indignant at The Beast's hieratic appearance; or even apparently outraged that he should slam his door upon a woman who had come to stay with him. On the contrary, their indignation was against her.

I could not, and indeed still cannot, explain this part of the story except on the assumption that they were not Catholics but followers of a pre-Christian cult which had come to recognise The Beast as their High Priest.

Betty May broke from them and beat on the door with her fists. After a time it opened once more. Again The Beast raised his wand and said, "Do what thou Wilt shall be the whole of the Law," in the Cockney accent which in that Mediterranean darkness must have been singularly menacing.

"Good evening," Betty May said.

"If you don't answer properly, I shan't let you in," he shouted.

"Love is the Law," muttered Betty May, "Love under Will."

She stepped across the threshold and the door closed on those swarthy Sicilian faces.

To become a member of the Order of the Abbey at Cefalu, it was necessary to sign adherence to the massive volume of rules, which lay upon the altar. Although do what thou wilt was the whole of the law, its interpretation involved a mass of regulations, which meant in brief that the whole of the law consisted in doing what The Beast willed. He was the only person allowed to refer to himself in the first person singular. The others were presented with razors and it was their duty in penance to gash their bodies when they used the forbidden 'I.' Betty May, though she signed her adherence to the Order, never observed this rule; but Loveday, or Adonis as he became known on his entrance to the Abbey, was soon a mass of scars.

I seized on the new name which Loveday was given at the Abbey as a clue to what was happening there and an indication as to why he was accompanied to the Abbey by a procession of Sicilians.

Before Christianity invaded Sicily, the island was principally the seat of the worship of the earth goddess Demeter and her daughter Persephone, who spent half the year in Hades and half on earth. If, as seemed likely, The Beast had discovered the survival of an ancient religion in Sicily, it was most probably the cult of Demeter and Persephone.

According to his myth, Adonis was beloved of two goddesses, Aphrodite and Persephone, with each of whom he spent half the year. He was the year-god, whose

annual death and resurrection were the ritual counter-
parts of the cycle of the sowing and the harvest, the
mystery of the seasons.

The razor-gashing which appeared to Betty May as
barbarous as it was absurd became significant if its object
was to obliterate the person of Raoul Loveday so that
Adonis could take over the tenancy of his body; and the
behaviour of the being whom Betty May still chose to
regard as her husband Raoul was explicable only if he had
become, or chose to consider that he was becoming,
Adonis.

The Beast, perceiving that Betty May had a natural distaste for lewdness and obscene language, would at some
meals devote himself exclusively to her, strewing before
her the contents of his cloacal mind without a word or
even a gesture of distaste from the young romantic to
whom she had been married.

There was something obviously very strange going on
at the Abbey. What it was Betty May did not know; indeed, it appeared as if she wasn't interested. What held
her to Cefalu was the struggle with The Beast for the
possession of her husband's body. While she remained
at the Abbey she could maintain the fiction that Raoul
was still hers. Though she was forced to attend the
Evening Pentagram, as the nightly ceremony was called
to distinguish it from the children's deviltry which was
led enthusiastically by 'little Lulu,' Betty May was present
only in the flesh. Her spirit was absent, yearning perhaps
for the gayer exhilaration of the Fitzroy Tavern or the
Harlequin. She went out of her way to break the rules of
the Abbey as a form of protest.

One evening at tea-time (a homely English meal from which even The Beast abroad did not divorce himself) just as they were about to eat, Crowley rose from his seat and going over to the brazier picked up one of the sacrificial knives, which he tested with his thumb. "Sister Sibylline will be sacrificed this evening," he remarked, and then turning to Betty, who had received this name on her induction, "You will be ready, Sister Sibylline."

Betty May looked at The Beast and then round the Thelemite circle, at the three women, plain Jane, fanatic Leah and the pregnant 'Shummy.' There was not a sign on their faces that anything in the least remarkable had been said. Adonis went on eating his tea without a flicker of sympathy.

"You really mean to kill me?" she asked.

"You are an evil spirit," The Beast said. "You cannot be allowed to remain in the Abbey to break every one of its rules in violation of the oath you took when signing the book."

After tea she stacked the cups and saucers in the sink and then went into the garden. While she was in sight of the house she walked slowly. But immediately she was out of sight she started to run along the paths among the rocks, with the lizards darting into cover and blue-winged cicadas rising up in panic. She ran up away from the farmhouse and the village and the railway that could take her to the safety of Palermo if she had the money and Italian to buy a ticket. She did not stop until she was high in the hills.

Night came up off the sea, like a cold, dark flood to engulf her; and little lights appeared in windows and grew brighter as the sun fell too low even to strike the clouds above.

The sacrificial knives were not beside the brazier for nothing. She had seen Adonis sacrifice a cat she had adopted, which The Beast had declared an evil spirit. 'Sacrifice' was too clean a word for an operation so incompetent; because though the animal had been etherised, it came to at the moment that Adonis tried to cut its throat, and escaping from his hand ran tearing and screeching round the Temple with blood spurting from its neck, and the whole incantation was repeated before the unfortunate beast was despatched and its blood drunk as a bestial sacrament. It was all very far from the Fitzroy Tavern with old Mr Kleinfeld rolling his belly down the bar like an eighteen-gallon cask with an imperial beard on top.

The dogs started to bark at each other across the valleys below and a cold wind came up from the sea. It grew too cold to be on a mountain and she made her way back to the Abbey. It was past midnight, but a light was still burning in the *Chambre des Cauchemars*. But the bedroom which Adonis now used was in darkness. This was a closet off the *Chambre des Cauchemars* to which Adonis could retire after he had done what The Beast wanted.

She reached out her hand to climb in through the window, and she felt her wrist gripped. "Don't be silly," said her husband; "it wasn't meant seriously."

It certainly wasn't a joke either.

I incline now to the view that they were all getting fed up with the way Sister Sibylline was behaving and The Beast wanted to give her a fright which would either scare her away or induce her to behave in future. But when I was at Oxford this explanation was too simple for my taste.

There were two ways in which Loveday could become Adonis. The first and more probable was that he became the human manifestation who killed the god in his animal manifestation (which of old was a wild boar, but perhaps in 1923, in view of the scarcity of wild boars, was the stray cat Mischette). The second, far more sensational, method which I preferred in my youth, was that Adonis became the devoted victim and in his human person suffered the god's passion. I clung, that is to say, to my brother's theory of the ritual sacrifice, but in a more devious way. Since Loveday died a 'natural' death, the only way I could have my ritual sacrifice was that Adonis was made to die, perhaps with his own connivance, in such a way that no blame would fall on the Abbey or The Beast.

The 'sacrifice' of Sister Sibylline, according to this theory, was an attempt to scare Betty May out of the Abbey; when it failed, a new plan had to be made. Betty May, the source of the greatest danger, was to be used to allay the suspicions of the two other danger-sources, the doctor at Cefalu and the British Consul at Palermo. The first thing was to convince her that she knew how Loveday contracted his fatal illness.

So one day The Beast sent her and Adonis to visit a monastery about twelve miles from the Abbey. "At the monastery they will give you to eat and drink," he said, "but on no account on your way there or back should you drink from any stream or spring, as the water is dangerous."

On the way back under the high sun they were both

consumed with thirst and coming to a spring which gushed out of the side of a hill Adonis fell on his knees and making a cup with his hands, he slaked his thirst.

Not long after this, but not so soon that she immediately connected it with The Beast's warning, Adonis fell sick, complaining of a heaviness in his limbs and a lassitude in his spirit. He no longer went into the garden and played with 'little Lulu' in the sunlight. All day long he sat in the Temple, trying to read a book, but taking nothing in.

When he saw this, The Beast did not summon a doctor. He said, "You are sick, Adonis. I will read your horoscope and tell you what the stars portend."

Later he came again with a grave face and said, "There is a great depression over you, Adonis. It looks as though you will die on the sixteenth of February at four o'clock. But you are young and perhaps you will recover."

So Betty May was prepared to believe that her husband was going to die as a result of disobeying The Beast's instructions and drinking spring water. Yet when the doctor was at last summoned, he found no signs of any forms of enteric fever, either because Adonis did not begin his mortal illness in that way or because the doctor was not summoned until complications had hidden the primary condition. It seemed to me that the doctor was called in not to cure Adonis but to certify that he was dying from natural causes.

The drama of Adonis was drawing to its climax, and there was a danger that even Sister Sibylline, who was bound to attend Pentagram, would realise that behind this mumbo-jumbo preparations were being made for the death of her husband. So The Beast issued an order that no newspapers should be read in the Abbey.

Betty May promptly disobeyed it, and The Beast, after she had tried to shoot him, picked her up in his arms, flung her like a sack of straw into the yard and told her never to come back.

It was a fantastic thing to do to a woman whose husband was lying on his deathbed; but from what followed it looked as if it was part of a deliberate plan. Betty May immediately went down to Cefalu, took a room for the night in one of the houses and sat down to write to the British Consul in Palermo a complete denunciation of Crowley and what he had done to her. While she was doing this, a woman from the Abbey, who must have been despatched soon after Betty May was thrown out, came into the room, read portions of her letter and went away, without trying to dissuade her from sending it to the Consul.

Next morning the same woman came back with a message, as she said, from Raoul, that unless she returned immediately, if necessary by stealth, he would certainly die. Betty May hurried back to the Abbey, to find The Beast waiting for her with a letter denying everything which she had said the day before to the Consul. Unless she signed that, he said, he forbade her to see Adonis.

By now distracted and hysterical, she signed it without even thinking that by doing so she had destroyed all chance of being treated as a credible witness and given the British Consul every reason to wash his hands of the whole sordid, contradictory affair.

What happened the night that Betty May spent at

Cefalu village I never made up my mind. Perhaps Loveday was not the willing victim I fancied, but was being made ill by The Beast, and the reason for her temporary expulsion was not magical but lethal. At least, when she saw him at last, Adonis was very much worse and the doctor was summoned once more. He prescribed an oil which was to be injected, and instead of sending either Jane or Leah to the village, The Beast despatched the dying man's wife, as though determined to keep her away from her husband at the end. Then having done so, as if he didn't trust her alone in the village, he followed her himself.

By this time Betty May was in a state of collapse. While she was waiting for the oil in the shop, she fainted, and when she came to, The Beast was standing over her. He had outside some sort of conveyance, in which they rode as close to the Abbey as the cart-track went; then in the declining light they set out on the last lap.

As the sun went down behind the mountain, The Beast halted and said the Adoration, as if to Adonis it was not a matter of life and death, but merely of the death about which The Beast knew before along the dusty winding path a woman from the Abbey came running to announce it.

For Betty May that moment was the end of the struggle which had started that night when Loveday had insisted on leaving her in order to meet The Beast. What happened after meant nothing to her.

Yet even she noticed that his death was the occasion for a tremendous outburst of magical activity. The body, in its open coffin, on the eve of interment was carried at sunset into an outhouse, and all night long The Beast in full robes performed some elaborate ritual around it.

The next day she watched the burial from a distance, as though it was the body not of her husband but of a stranger that was being buried. A site had been chosen on unhallowed ground just without the walls of the Catholic cemetery on the hillside. Accompanied by the three weird women of his order, the High Priest, with his rich robes gleaming and his theatrical rings flashing in the sunlight, conducted the ceremony.

They were not alone. From farmstead and stray villages on the hills, from Cefalu and from Palermo and elsewhere assembled a congregation, to pay, as Betty May thought, a touching tribute to the young Englishman who had come to their island so few months ago. It was not Raoul's funeral they were attending, I suspected, but the older obsequies of the god beloved by Aphrodite and the daughter of Earth, whose image was tossed at Alexandria with lamentation into the sea and whose blood mingling with the earth brought the corn-ears to fullness; a strange apotheosis for the young man who loved wine-dark roses, revelled in wetness, proposed marriage with the threat of murder and crowned the Oxford martyrs with a chamber-pot.

Part Three

THE HOME OF LOST CURSES

Chapter Six

Hugh

*

I THOUGHT of Hugh the moment I read the remark of Madame Blavatsky to William Butler Yeats: "I used to wonder at and pity the people who sell their souls to the devil. But now I only pity them. They do it to have somebody on their side."

Hugh was the first person I noticed when, as a result of writing for University papers, I began to be invited to Oxford as opposed to intercollege parties. He always seemed to be there, however much the other company changed, like the outside waiter of the only caterer in a provincial town.

He had hair most beautiful in colour, a sort of burnished gold, which attracted notice from a distance. It shone in the street a quarter of a mile away like an invitation from a heliograph, and as you walked towards him he was marked out for scrutiny even in the middle of a crowd.

This was a pity, because his only chance of ordinary happiness lay in being unobtrusive. His face had never 'fined out'; it had the blobbiness found in many children during the first two years of life. And his teeth were very bad. They were dark brown towards the roots and there was some argument about whether their colour was predominantly yellow or green, and whether their texture was harsh, furry or slimy. Yet there was no doubt how bad anyone with a hangover felt when he said, "I feel like Hugh's teeth."

The drawback of his beautiful hair was that everybody who met him for the first time was disappointed. He was at his best in sunlight at a distance of between four hundred-and-forty and three hundred-and-thirty yards. His hair, in fact, held such promise that by the time people met him face to face they were angry at having been hoaxed.

It inhibited Hugh because he liked meeting new people and yet he could sympathise with how they felt when they looked at him. If there was a mirror in the room, he kept turning round sharply trying to catch himself not looking so plain, but he never did. Sometimes he looked at himself in a mirror for a long time, hoping his unloveliness would vanish, like a pimple. But there was his early Saxon image staring him out of countenance, like a windchapped churl. He was an unhappy youth.

I was surprised that he should be invited to so many parties, because he himself seldom entertained. Yet there he always was, sipping his cocktail and talking in a rather solemn way, like a nineteenth-century imitation of the eighteenth. He posed a mystery that I did not particularly want to solve. His conversation was not brilliant, nor at first hearing memorable. Yet it was strangely stinging. It could bring me out into a psychological nettle-rash hours or even days later.

The first party which I held gave me a clue to his apparent popularity. I hadn't asked him, because he had never entertained me and I never wanted him to. But he was the third person to arrive. He scarcely troubled to feign surprise. "Oh," he said, though he had never called on me before, "you're giving a party. I'm awfully sorry. If you'd only told me, I'd have kept away."

"Now you've come," I said, "of course you must stay."

Later in the evening, another guest arriving said, "Well, well, well, Hugh! So you managed to gate-crash in the end."

Hugh looked across at me, saw that I had heard, and winked at me in complicity against our host. I winked back and only later remembered that the host was I.

I thought at first that Hugh, because he was not a very attractive person, got more enjoyment out of parties than people whose private lives are more satisfying. He wanted company because he had small chance of winning love. But as he developed the habit of 'dropping in' at odd and often inconvenient times I found there was more to it than that.

His father was in the antique business, and Hugh had acquired the social philosophy common to trades which involve the lightning assessment of whether people have anything worth selling or the money to buy from those who have. He knew a certain amount about furniture and painting, but as he wasn't going into the family business, he wasn't interested in people's material possessions so much as their 'contacts.' He looked round any room he entered to see who was there who might be useful. He regarded it almost as a professional right.

One day he told me with pride of a revenge he had taken against an Austrian Count and a Polish Prince, the first of whom had incurred his displeasure by not inviting him to a party which 'absolutely everyone' had attended, and the second of whom had ejected him from a party to which he had not been invited.

"You can understand," Hugh said, "it was a thing I couldn't forgive." From each of his enemies he had stolen notepaper. On the Count's he wrote an insulting note to the Prince and forged the Count's signature. On the Prince's he wrote a challenge to a duel. By a series of complicated interceptions and counterfeitings, he had brought his two enemies face to face with one another in a ground-floor room where he could observe their meeting from the pavement.

It was a very long story and I didn't listen to the half of it, because I didn't believe that anyone could go to such pains to pay off injuries which he had only suffered through intrusiveness.

"When they met in the room, Hugh," I asked, "did they have a duel?"

"At one moment they very nearly came to blows," he said; "they were both very angry."

"But later?"

"Later they embraced one another and the Count produced a bottle of champagne and they toasted one another." He looked rather shamefaced.

"What a pity for you! You go to all that trouble and then all you succeed in doing is to draw them closer together than they've ever been. Isn't that a waste of time?"

His face suddenly brightened. "I hadn't thought of that," he said. "They scarcely knew one another before. But when I went away they seemed to be very good friends. You might say, really, that I brought them together. Come to think of it, they ought to be grateful to me."

If he couldn't do them any harm, he was prepared to do good. He had altered a situation. He was not neutral. And perhaps when he explained to them later how he had arranged for them to make friends, they would both invite him to their next parties.

I paid very little attention to this story of Hugh's at the time. The human mind is very like a Civil Servant's In-tray. Anything that does not demand immediate action is initialled and returned to Registry. Deciding glibly that Hugh would have been happier at the court of the Borgias, I filed away the memory.

But shortly afterwards I had reason to consult it again.

A group in my own college approached me to join a study circle in ritual magic, and though I didn't like the idea I agreed. I could not make up my mind whether to approach magic as Frazer and others had, as a very primitive attempt to explain and influence natural fertility, or, as Crowley and Vickybird believed, as a means of reaching affinity with the elemental powers. But one thing I was certain of after our first meeting was that to listen to papers which were inaccurate digests of the anthropologists whom I had read was a waste of time.

To say so would have been arrogant, and when it came to my turn to read a paper I looked round for a means of breaking away. There was a chance of writing a paper on Incubi and Succubi, based on the work of the Reverend Father Sinistrari of Ameno, whose old Latin text I had acquired in Brighton, with an English translation. There were some girls from Somerville in the group, and it would have been possible to make the paper obscene enough to have bust the group for good, because they were emotionally as prim as they were intellectually broad-minded. But they were nice girls and I didn't want to cause them embarrassment.

For the same reason I rejected a paper on the incidence of supernumerary nipples among witches and warlocks of the seventeenth century compared with those of conscripts in the First World War. It could only have put an end to the futile group by being so crude that it wouldn't have been funny to write.

So there was only one choice. When asked the subject of my paper, I said that the time for theory had passed. The next stage was practice. The Coven would meet in my rooms that day next week for its first practical. This was an enunciation of a tactic which I had recently evolved, *sauter pour mieux reculer*. As soon as I left the room, I heard the women's voices raised in protest. 'With any luck,' I thought, 'we shan't even have to have a practical.'

The next day a deputation of warlocks came to plead that the time was not yet ripe for practice. The witches felt they didn't yet know enough. "Tell them," I said, "that you can no more understand the theory of magic without practising it than you can understand Freud without being psycho-analysed. As a concession, shall we say that we don't convene the Coven in full Sabbath this time, but just have an informal Esbath."

"What's that?" they asked.

"Well," I said vaguely, "you might call it a Black Mattins."

Certain that the witches would back out, I was growing over-confident. For when the warlocks returned to say that the girls from Somerville wished to be excused Black Mattins, I said, "Of course I could easily get some more witches, but I expect you want to call the whole thing off. It would probably be better, anyway."

To my horror, they protested that they were most anxious to proceed with the practical work and left it to me to make full arrangements. I was hoist with my own petard.

The only properties I had which could be of any use were Auntie Helen's candlesticks and incense-burner, which had taken periodic sanctuary in a suitcase under my bed. From Mowbray's I obtained black candles, a packet of unconsecrated wafers and a number of incense-cones which smouldered sulkily in the unventilated incense-burner with a smell like smoking rope.

Jim Wyllie, who ran a discreet café called the Moorish, knocked off a series of indiscreet designs in poster-paints on drawer-paper. These, pinned to the walls, lent my college room an air if not diabolical at least heterodox. A liturgy in mediæval Latin was specially composed by a friend who threw himself eagerly into the ceremony and insisted on contributing the parings of his toenails and other trimmings from his body to be burnt in the incense bowl. Since the ceremony, I was convinced, would be as boring to attend as it would be amusing to gossip about, I arranged that as soon as it ended a plentiful supply of gin and sherry should be available to heal the painful memory with strong doses of alcohol.

From Lady Margaret Hall was recruited an attractive band of witches to replace the timorous apostates of Somerville; and all was set for a quiet little Esbath which would make our boring study circle disappear like magic.

But I was reckoning without Hugh, to whom I had mentioned the affair as an example of the absurd quandaries in which over-subtlety could place one. His curiosity was immediately aroused. Eager for notoriety, he imagined various ways in which it could be converted into a University joke of classic proportions. "But you haven't invited me," he said.

"We've got too many men already," I answered, "and anyway, even though it's only a bit of nonsense, it's probably just as well that a Catholic like you shouldn't be mixed up in it."

Both the excuses were valid, but to a person as sensitive to slight as Hugh was, they carried no weight. He knew that the reason why he had not been invited was the usual one. He just wasn't wanted.

"I believe you're going to celebrate the Black Mass," he said.

"Don't be an ass."

He shook his head gravely and went out of the room.

That evening I was dining at the George, and a dozen people came up to ask whether it was true that I was celebrating Black Mass the next day. They had all got it at first or second hand from Hugh, who on the strength of the story had gained entry to three different cocktail parties to which he hadn't been invited. His tactics were infinitely adaptable. He was turning a joke which he had not been invited to share into an act of blasphemy which he abhorred; and the social contacts which he had hoped to make by joining in he was making instead by standing out.

The harm was already done. Gossip spreads faster through Oxford than round a Cathedral close. But I was so angry with Hugh, that he should deliberately spread a lie that might get me and perhaps all of us sent down, that I went round to his college immediately after dinner.

He was not of course in his rooms; he was going the rounds of Oxford, publishing the scandal with the same vengeful thoroughness he had displayed towards the grandees who had snubbed him. I left him a rude note telling him to come to my rooms next day before lunch; it was so rude that when I was half-way to my college I thought I had defeated my purpose. Even Hugh wouldn't stomach it.

But next morning at twelve-thirty he came sidling into my room. He didn't look me in the face and I thought that he was abashed until I realised that he was surveying the room for evidence of the ceremony to be held later. He had not come in answer to my note but because he wanted the latest information on the story. "It was nice of you to ask me round for a drink before lunch," he said. In a rather galling way he was treating the note as if it was a lapse in taste which he was prepared to overlook.

As I poured him a sherry he went to my bedroom and opened the door. "What a nice sunny room you have here," he said, peering behind the wardrobe. "My bedroom faces north and it's icy."

"If you want this sherry," I said, "you'd better come and get it."

He reluctantly turned away from the chest of drawers where the indiscreet cartoons were hidden and came back into the living-room. As I handed him his glass, I said, "What the hell do you mean by spreading this silly story about a Black Mass after what I told you yesterday?"

"Isn't it true?"

"Are you saying I lied?"

"When you told me yesterday that you couldn't invite me because I was a Catholic, there was only one conclusion I could draw."

"There are other conclusions."

He raised his glass, looking me for the first time in the eyes. "Such as?" he asked, daring me to tell the truth.

"That I didn't want you," I said; then, seeing the pain on his homely face, I added, "People would invite you more often, if you weren't so eager to be invited everywhere always."

He walked over to the window. "It may interest you to know that Father Ronald Knox is taking the affair so seriously that he spent all night on his knees before the altar praying that you should suffer a change of heart."

I laughed. "I'm not a Catholic, but I'm sure that Father Knox couldn't be such an ass."

He finished his sherry and put down his glass. Then he came across to me and with great solemnity said, "I do implore you to reconsider what you are doing, for *my* sake."

"Why for *your* sake?"

He shrugged his shoulders. "One is one's brother's keeper."

"I could bear almost anything but that, Hugh."

My scout came in with a roll, butter and cheese on a plate. He set it down on the table. "Will there be anything else, sir?" he asked, glancing at Hugh.

"No, thank you," I said. "I am lunching alone."

Hugh went to the door. "When, by the way, is it going to take place?"

"When could it be, save at the setting of the sun?"

"What time is that?"

"Look up Lighting-up Time in your diary," I suggested.

I never discovered whether it was Father Knox or Hugh who telephoned the Dean. But at approximately sunset there was a knock on my door and I opened it to the senior porter, who left his winter quarters, the lodge, only at the behest of the highest powers, and then sulkily. "The Dean wancher," he said and then, as he was halfway down the stairs, "Toot sweet."

I was glad that the ceremony had been concluded an hour previously and all the sabbatical properties cleared away, before I was asked to see the Dean. In full session the Black Mattins might have appeared to his eyes more sinister than absurd.

The Dean was famous for his charm and admired for his firm and graceful handling of the indecorous subjects which he had occasionally to discuss with undergraduates. I had never seen him discomposed until that evening.

He asked me to sit down. He gave me a cigarette. He remarked on the brilliance of the weather for the time of year.

I observed that the English climate was so changeable

that one couldn't qualify any observation about the weather by 'the time of the year' because this implied a norm which did not exist, except as a meaningless average between extremes.

"Are you holding a Black Mass in your room?" he interrupted with the equivocal expression of a man who is not sure whether the question he is asking is very silly or very serious.

I laughed. "Of course not, sir."

He joined in the laughter for a moment; then with a sudden return to gravity, like a twinge of flatulence, he said, "But you are holding some sort of . . . er . . . Sabbath, I take it."

"Not a Sabbath, sir!" I said firmly. "Purely an informal Esbath."

"A what?"

"The best distinction between a Sabbath and an Esbath, sir, is to be found in Miss Murray's *Witch-cult in Western Europe*. If you'd like to borrow . . ."

"What I want to know is, Did you have the Consecrated Host and a defrocked priest?"

"No, sir. The only defrocked priest I know lives in Hove and he's too old to get about much. We had tinned spider-crab from Kamchatka and a dry Amontillado. Actually, there is some left, if you'd like to come up . . ."

The Dean brushed aside the offer of the crumbs from the warlocks' table; but he seemed reassured by the invitation. "Then you can assure me there was nothing sacrilegious or blasphemous about this whatever-you-call-it."

"It was probably, sir, the tamest Esbath ever."

He stood up. The interview was at an end. "I take your word for it," he said, "but I think it would be a good idea if this didn't happen again."

"I assure you, sir, there will be no need for another. This one achieved its purpose admirably."

Just as I was going out of the door, he said, "And what was the purpose?"

"I suppose you might say, sir," I answered, "that it was to dispel the depression caused by the hebdomadal conjunction of ponderous spirits."

After the Black Mattins I decided to see no more of Hugh. He had failed to have me sent down, but it wasn't for lack of trying. That in itself was sufficient ground for breaking with the fellow even if his company had been entertaining.

I cut him several times in the street and turned my back on him at a party or two. I just didn't spit in his eye.

There began to arrive in my rooms a succession of envoys to plead his cause, all the more irritating because their attitude was that I was in the wrong. After all, I hadn't been sent down; so what really was there to complain about? It was very silly surely to make all this fuss about something which had never happened.

A series of futile arguments took place, which wasted even more time than Hugh himself had when he dropped in. I refused to give way until Hugh admitted that what he had done, if not malevolent, was injudicious. But each new advocate protested that I was being grossly unjust in thrusting aside an old and faithful friend.

It was a situation that became daily more ridiculous, in view of the fact that I had never regarded him as more than an acquaintance who had more time to spare than I had.

Then one evening he came to my rooms as I was working on an essay due for a tutorial early the next morning. At such a moment no one was welcome. "I'm busy," I said, "please go away."

But with triumph glinting in his eye he came over to the table where I was working and produced from under his arm a copy of *Punch*. He opened it at the Charivaria page and passed it to me. Round one item had been drawn an ovoid in blue crayon.

> "A Black Mass was held last week in Oxford. It seems that the Home of Lost Causes has become the Home of Lost Curses."

"What did they pay you for that?" I asked; "half a guinea?"

He looked at me with an expression of pain and pity which I came later to recognise as the look which publicity agents reserve for clients who don't understand that any publicity however bad is good. "I can't understand why you are angry with me, after all I've done for you," he said. "Nobody would have heard of that silly affair of yours the other week, if it hadn't been for me. Now everybody's talking about it. It's even in *Punch*."

"Surely you can understand when I say I know what you really did and what your motives were."

He folded up the copy of *Punch*. "Anyway you deserved it," he said. "If you'd invited me, I wouldn't have come. Whatever you may think, I'm a good Catholic. But you didn't ask me."

Suddenly I saw that I had been wrong to think of Hugh as a sort of Iago, a subordinate figure of pure malevolence whose importance lies in precipitating trouble. Hugh was made from the same stuff as Judas. It was as natural for him to betray those he liked as it was for Judas to choose a kiss as the means of marking down his Master. Hugh's envoys had been right; he regarded me as a friend, perhaps could not have behaved so badly if he didn't. There was nothing inconsistent in his actions. "All right," I said. "Let's forget it. But I really *am* busy tonight."

His red, shifty face was illuminated for a moment by a sort of magnesium-ribbon smile which gave it an eerie distinction. "I'll go now," he said.

As his footsteps died away on the bare boards of my passage, I tried to recapture the mood of my comparison of Queen Teuta of Macedonia with Queen Elizabeth of England. But before I could do so, the footsteps returned and the door opened. "I am glad in a way that this happened," Hugh's head said. "I think it will bring us closer together."

Hugh was right. The incident brought us far closer together, though on my side there was no affection. I watched him with suspicion, curiosity and a repugnant admiration. But I came to regard him as part of my life, like an incurable skin infection. I never knew where he was going to break out next.

At one moment he would seem as single and devoted a character as Raoul Loveday or Auntie Helen, except that his pursuit was not of victimage or love but notoriety in its crudest form, or even villainy. At the next he would reveal a loyalty or tenderness which seemed completely out of character.

Like me, he had an elder brother, and with the same name. This brother was in every way his opposite, dark-haired, handsome, well formed and gifted with a most beautiful voice. Hugh adored him as if he was his own soul, free of the chains which nature had laid on him. Hugh's voice changed when he spoke of his brother and its tone became pleasing, so that one realised that its usual grating was not natural, but caused by the harsh contact it made with reality.

Yet his overruling passion, to get on, to be noticed at any cost, to soar into Society, made him regard his brother as a treasury of social contacts.

There were many petty Hughs in Oxford, snobs who regarded society as a ladder to be climbed laboriously, people who were only too glad to kick the friends of yesterday in the teeth in order to secure the friends of to-morrow. Compared to them, Hugh was a generous person, because he did not aim to climb to the top on the backs of other people. It was too slow. He preferred a balloon. With Giles Playfair as his President and co-Founder, he became the Honorary Treasurer of the Oxford Balloon Club.

The apparent significance of the Oxford Balloon Club was that it had no point. The time had passed when young men in Norfolk jackets and knickerbockers, with handlebar moustaches and multi-purpose caps, had ascended from the ground in lighter-than-air-craft to fire the imagination of their earthbound audience with the possibilities of ascension. A balloon ascent in the late twenties was as silly as bicycling to Brighton on a bone-shaker or racing from John O'Groats to Lands End in the original horseless carriage. "All the Press will be there," Hugh said; "we shall have nation-wide coverage."

The plan was that one afternoon from the neighbour-hood of the gasworks, which was handy for inflation, a balloon should go up, drift with the wind and come down again. "The snag is so few people can go in a balloon," Hugh said, "so we are giving a banquet beforehand to de-fray the cost of inflation. How many tickets would you like?"

"It's the silliest idea I've ever heard," I said. "And you expect me to shell out an exorbitant sum for an indifferent meal so that you and Giles can gallivant in a balloon on the difference!"

"You're approaching this in the wrong spirit, Arthur," he said. "Your parents are paying a lot of money to keep you at Oxford. Your duty to them is to use every oppor-tunity to meet people who will help you when you go down."

"What's that got to do with sending you and Giles up in a balloon?"

Hugh sighed. "Giles and I would give up our places in the balloon with the greatest of pleasure, but clearly the President and Treasurer of the club must rise in the in-augural basket. With any luck we shall get Tallulah Bankhead as a member of the crew. That only leaves room for the man who knows how to work the beastly thing. But I do promise you, when there is the second flight, you shall have first place. What about four tickets?"

"Why on earth should I buy four tickets?"

"How silly of me to suggest it!" Hugh said. "Of course, you'd prefer just one ticket, so that you can move among the distinguished guests without the encumbrance of a party."

I had never seen Hugh in this particular rôle before, and I was bewildered.

"Sir Nigel is one of the most influential people in London," he went on, "and for Giles's sake he is putting his full weight behind this; and my brother is bringing a most distinguished party—you'll meet him at the lunch. The balloon, you see, is just a bait to get important people up from London. It's a chance of meeting the people who matter which you mustn't miss."

"I see what you're getting at," I said.

"I was sure you would—in the end. Then how many tickets will you take?"

"None."

Hugh held his banquet, and a lot of stage people turned up. There weren't quite so many as Hugh hoped, nor were they quite so distinguished. They were actors and actresses whose names were not currently appearing in the weekly papers. It was a *concours de publicité*, which was covered by the less sophisticated papers, and both Hugh and Giles featured prominently.

"I'm very glad you've established the Balloon Club," I said to Hugh, when I had read the press. "When is your next ascent?"

"There won't be another one," he said.

"You must have made quite a decent thing out of the first."

"We didn't do badly," he agreed. "But you can't work a stunt like that twice. Next time it'd have to be a dirigible. And that of course is out of the question. Besides, we'd have to go somewhere. And then we'd have to do something. And we haven't got the capital for that. Anyway there's no point."

"What *did* you make out of it?" I asked.

"It's really the fun of the thing that matters," Hugh said. "And it was fun."

"But as the Treasurer of a University Society you'll have to render accounts, you know."

"Giles and I were the only members anyway," he said, "so what does it matter?" He began to show alarm.

"Are you registered as a profit-making company?" I asked. "What about income tax? There are all sorts of things."

Hugh looked very guilty. "Will you promise not to laugh at me?"

"Why?"

"I've got a confession to make. We didn't make any money at all. We should have done if I had taken cash for all the seats at the banquet. But I took cheques and promises and I'm out of pocket." He was like a child with a Victorian kaleidoscope. He shook it and converted an enviable profit into a pitiful loss. "Don't tell Giles about this," he said, "because I told him we broke about even, but if he knew that I'd paid the loss out of my pocket, he'd be terribly worried. He'd want to make up the difference out of his own pocket, and I know he's broke."

"That is extraordinarily nice of you, Hugh."

"It is a thing you will never give me credit for," he said. "But I'm not as mean and hard as you are."

As soon as the Balloon Club had ended, Hugh began to look round for another vehicle for his genius. He didn't like long-established societies. The competition for office was too strong and his own qualifications were slender. He achieved somehow the publication of a thin volume of essays; whether his father had footed the printer's bill, I never discovered. But though the talent was tenuous, no one dared criticise openly who had not appeared in book form. Keith Winter and Derek Walker-Smith, the only two who had, were diplomatic enough to keep their mouths shut. Meanwhile Hugh was biding his time.

One day he said to me, "Do you realise that we haven't got a literary workshop, or rather showroom, in Oxford? There are hundreds of people here who want to write. But they never meet one another."

"Isn't that rather a good thing?" I asked. "If they did, they'd write about one another, like D. H. Lawrence, Katherine Mansfield and Middleton Murry."

"There's a man whom nobody's ever heard of except me," Hugh said. "He loves Beauty and writes poems and he's asked everybody who loves Beauty and writes poems to come and see him on Thursday evening."

"Meaning one ought?"

"Meaning one must," Hugh said. "I think our parents would never forgive us if we didn't avail ourselves of this opportunity."

I forget the name of the young man who loved Beauty.

But I remember blonde wavy hair, a black velvet smoking-jacket and a white powdered face. He was a bit like Gilbert's poet, Bunthorne, in *Patience*; but with it all he was a very gentle creature, pained and puzzled by the rejection of poems which his friends studying Eng. Lit. agreed were almost indistinguishable from those selected by Quiller-Couch for the *Oxford Book of English Verse*.

Instead of wondering whether this was not the reason for his manifold rejection and emigrating to an Oriental country where imitation of ancestors ranked as the highest virtue, he had issued his invitation hoping to add another dozen to his listeners.

He had under-estimated Hugh's ability as a promoter and the numbers of would-be poets hiding in the academic undergrowth, who when they heard his call left their dens like the shy beasts when Orpheus played his lute. His room held sixty people with difficulty, and about a hundred and fifty fought to get within earshot. In terms of discomfort, the standard measure of success, the meeting was a triumph. It was also exciting as a mass meeting of recluses and solitaries, a congregation of the ungregarious brought about by the desire to break down the barriers of isolation. Hugh, with his nose for a good thing, had been right.

The Oxford University Poetry Society was founded that evening for the purpose of reading and criticising poems written by the members. The young man who loved Beauty became its Secretary, Clere Parsons, the editor of *Oxford Poetry*, its President. But for a moment it seemed as if the new Society would founder for lack of an Honorary Treasurer. Poet after poet was approached;

but each confessed to a pathological inability to collect money or keep accounts.

Finally Hugh, who by his early arrival had seized a strategic position by a window, caught the attention of the President. "Ladies and gentlemen, and Mr President, sir," he said, "I should be unhappy to see this Society, which has just been founded on the resolution of one of the most stirring gatherings it has been my privilege to attend, die at birth for lack of a Treasurer. I myself am not a poet but an essayist, and so am hesitant to thrust myself forward. But as the Honorary Treasurer of the Oxford Balloon Club, I have had some experience of these matters, and if the services of no poet can be enlisted, I am prepared to offer the slender gifts of a mere essayist for this office."

This speech, so humble and so helpful, was greeted with clapping and cheers. Hugh was unanimously elected and received the gratitude of the Society with a modest bow. "There is just one thing," he added, "which I must make clear from the start. This Society will be a success only if you are all regular and punctual in the payment of your subscriptions. In the case of the Balloon Club, owing to certain people promising but then failing to pay their contributions, we were left with a considerable deficit, which I made good out of my own purse. That, ladies and gentlemen, cannot happen again, because . . ." he flashed a furry smile, ". . . I am not made of money, you know."

As I left the meeting with Hugh, I said, "How very generous of you to volunteer, after your unfortunate experience with the Balloon Club!"

Hugh

"One couldn't stand by and see that splendid enthusiasm run to waste!" he said modestly. "I felt it was the least I could do, seeing that I can't write poetry myself."

I had smoked all my cigarettes and I went part of the way with Hugh, to get some more from a slot-machine outside a tobacconist's. "I must say I was rather surprised at your publicly mentioning the financial loss, when you were so anxious to hide it from Giles."

"Considering that you'd already told him, Arthur, I didn't feel it made very much difference."

"I never mentioned a word to Giles. You asked me not to. Don't you remember?"

"Then it wasn't *you*?" he said. "I'm so relieved. But anyway someone told him, and he came round to see me, so miserable until I persuaded him to forget about it."

We had reached the tobacconist's and I put a shilling in the machine and pulled out the drawer. "I suppose I'd better get some," Hugh said, fumbling in his pocket without success. "I say, don't you think it would be a nice idea to pay me your subscription now? Then you'd be the foundation member."

"No," I said, "but I can lend you sixpence."

The poetry readings were not a good idea. It seemed a rule that the better the poet, the worse the reciter, and the worse the poem the finer it sounded on first hearing. The Society from the beginning was split into two groups, and the poetic criticism and discussions degenerated into endless bickering about the æsthetic qualities of the Oxford gasworks.

The chief merit of the Poetry Society seemed to reside

not in its public meetings, but in the fact that it had introduced to one another sooner people who would anyway have met later. I gave it a term to live. But once again I reckoned without Hugh. At the moment when the Society was about to disband in mutual exasperation, Hugh made his financial statement. "Ladies and Gentlemen and Mr President, sir," he said, "as your Honorary Treasurer I am glad to inform you that the Society has a certain balance. The exact figures for the moment elude me; but we have sufficient to our credit to make practicable the proposal which I shall lay before you, should you approve it.

"A Society like ours is a growing thing. We came together with the desire to meet our fellow writers, discuss our problems and pool our experience.

"Speaking as an outsider, I believe that we have gone as far in that direction as it is possible for us to go. It seems to me that the time has now come for us to listen to the voices of experience, to invite the most distinguished of our living poets to come and talk to us, not in the rather formal way that lecturers address the English Society, but intimately as older craftsmen talking to the rising generation, the writers of tomorrow."

After very little discussion Hugh's proposal was adopted; and nobody thought to observe that as a financial statement it could scarcely have been more vague. Our Honorary Treasurer was in a curious position of power. He held office because no one else was prepared to take over his tedious duties; and there was no sense in questioning his sketchy accountancy unless there was a candidate to succeed him.

Even when I became Secretary of the Poetry Society, I remained incurious of its finances. Two or three times at dinners Hugh forgot to bring along his cheque-book to pay the bill and I paid it for him, thinking that, for a person as improvident as myself, this was an excellent method of saving. What I lent to the Poetry Society I couldn't squander myself. By the end of term I had saved eight pounds in this fashion, and I called on Hugh to collect it.

"I'm awfully sorry," he said, "but the Poetry Society hasn't any more money."

"What the hell do you mean?"

"I thought you knew," he said; "I was going to ask the Society to propose a vote of thanks to you for your generosity."

"You know perfectly well I didn't know."

"Everyone else did. Why do you think I said I hadn't any money at the end of those dinners?"

"Where are your accounts?"

"Well, as a matter of fact," Hugh said, "the whole thing was so simple. Just collecting money from people and spending it. I didn't bother to keep any accounts. After all, the only important thing is that there isn't any money left. No amount of accounts can alter that."

Eight pounds may not seem a very great sum, but twenty years ago it was worth four times what it is today, and it was all the money I had till the end of the month. I was very angry with Hugh for playing on the Poetry Society the same trick he had played on the Balloon Club, and with myself for letting him get away with it. "You're a crook, Hugh," I said, "and I'm going to see that people know it."

He remained very calm. "How?"

"I shall call a meeting of the Society."

"There isn't time to call one before the end of the term."

"I shall call it next term."

"No one will turn up to a meeting who knows that you're going to pass the hat round to collect eight quid for yourself."

"I shall go to the Proctors, then."

"Of course you know them, don't you?" he said. "What was the last thing you saw them about? Some woman of the town, wasn't it, whom they thought undesirable? Of course, it'll only be my word against yours. They might believe you."

It was impossible to be angry any longer. He had thought of everything. "Eight pounds," he said, "is a trifling sum to break a friendship for, and I do assure you that if I had any money at all, I'd go fifty-fifty with you. But the truth is . . . well, there's a chap in my college . . . he's the son of a miner, on scholarships, you know. His father's got silicosis and . . . you'll probably think I'm sentimental . . . but I lent him everything I'd got . . . there's precious little hope of his being able to pay it back."

"I don't think you're sentimental," I said. "What is silicosis?"

"It's something miners get. I'm not quite sure what, but jolly nasty. Sort of fossilised lungs, I think."

"I suppose you lent him eight pounds?"

"As a matter of fact, it was twenty," he said; "so you see how I'm fixed."

I laughed. As a lie, it was almost worth eight quid. Hugh was wasting himself on writing essays. Fiction was his *métier*. "I can't help admiring you, Hugh," I said.

"I hope you didn't think I told you about this chap because I wanted your admiration," he said; "there is nobody I dislike more than the person who goes round bragging about any little act of decency he may have done. I merely wanted you to understand why I couldn't defray this loss you've incurred." His manner was changing swiftly, like a canoe that has shot the rapids coming into calm water. He poured me out a drink. "And now that little affair is settled," he said, handing me a glass of sherry, "let us get down to what I really want to ask you. I'm having my twenty-firster in the middle of next month. And I'd like you to come to it, as my greatest friend."

"I didn't quite catch that?"

"As my greatest friend," he repeated. "In fact, you're the only person from the University I'm inviting. Most of the other people are friends of my brother's; influential people, of course."

"Where are you holding this?" I asked.

"Well," he said, "instead of having one of those affairs at the Berkeley, I thought it might be rather amusing if we had dinner at John Fothergill's. He's got a nice private room in the back of the Spreadeagle."

"To go all the way up to Thame in the vacation, purely for dinner, seems going a bit far, doesn't it?"

"Oh, it doesn't matter, if it's too much bother," he said, "I just wondered . . ."

I couldn't bear the sight of his hangdog Saxon look. If I was his greatest friend, in what an arctic climate of unlove he dwelt! "I shall be very pleased to come, Hugh. I feel oddly touched."

At the same time, I felt curious. If not parsimonious, Hugh had always been rather close. To invite a party of a dozen people to dine and spend the night at the Spread-eagle seemed hardly possible for a man who had given his last twenty pounds to the son of a silicotic miner. Perhaps the funds of the Poetry Society were larger than I had imagined.

Pleasantly stiff and old-fashioned, the dinner was excellent while it lasted. But at eight forty-five, when we had each finished a glass of port, Hugh suddenly intimated that dinner was over. He was no longer our host. If we wanted to have anything more to drink, then it was up to us.

The next morning Hugh came up to me after breakfast. "I'm settling up for all of us," he said; "it's far easier than having a lot of separate bills."

"Of course," I said. "How much do you want?"

"Oh, give me four pounds," he said; "we'll forget about the odd silver."

"Isn't that very expensive?"

"Don't forget, this is a first-class hotel," he answered. "They've got a copy of *Decline and Fall* in the lavatory. If you haven't got the cash, just make me out a cheque."

I distrust most ætiological explanations, because it is so easy to read back into past events meanings which were not present at the time. If I had been asked at Oxford to forecast Hugh's future, I should have predicted a long and notorious career of repeated betrayals and petty dishonesty, never being very far from prison, but never entering it, an inevitable figure in literary life, the secretary of a wine-tasting society, the founder of a dining club dedicated to the memory of Edward Gibbon, each member of which would be known by the name of a Cæsar, the discoverer of an important manuscript which was not detected as a forgery in his lifetime, the collector of some neglected trivia, such as door-knobs, hatpins or spectacle-cases, a monograph on which Messrs Batsford would commission him to write in his late fifties. I might even have prophesied that fifty years after his death when his name had disappeared even from the footnotes of the minor biographies of his period, he would win a posthumous fame as his diaries presented to the British Museum on his death revealed on publication a startling picture of his times in the distorting mirror of his mind.

But knowing as I do that within a year of leaving Oxford he was dead of a tubercle whose invasions must have been in progress when I knew him, I am tempted to believe that his greed for notoriety, his galloping ambition and his hunger for company were due to a premonition that his residence on earth was brief and he had no time for the leisurely enjoyments savoured by those whose stay is longer.

Chapter Seven

Laughter in the Broad

*

WHEN I asked Vickybird if he would come to speak to the Poetry Society, he immediately said No. He was an old fogey, he was a back number, he was a P.I.B. (Poor Ignorant Bastard).

"Is Aleister Crowley a back number?" I asked. "Because we've invited him too. And he's accepted."

"No," he said, "you mustn't do that. It'd be madness. Haven't I told you over and over again that he's an extremely dangerous man?"

"I know you have," I said, "but you've never told me why. I'd've thought you'd object to his use of drugs, but you don't."

"I've told you over and over again that he has betrayed his trust. There is white magic and there is black; and he has chosen the powers of darkness."

"Something must have made you change your mind about him," I said, "but you've never told me what it was."

"I've never told you," he said, "because I am not sure that you would understand. Magic is like any other form of experience. You cannot explain it to anyone who has had no experience of it, and to those who have there is no need to explain. But the next time we go for a walk together, I'll tell you what happened."

"That's a promise," I said, "but meanwhile what about coming to Oxford?"

He pointed to his coat and knickerbockers. "In this garb, my dear sir? You are very loyal, but I don't think you'd be proud to exhibit me to your clever Oxford friends attired in the habiliments of a scarecrow or Tomnoddy. Far be it from me to play the swell or macaroni. But I'm not so rustic that I've lost the sense of cum-eel-foh. Sartorially, it's out."

"If I can get you a suit," I said, "will you promise to come?" I had in my wardrobe a blue serge suit which I had not worn since I left school. It was in good condition, but blue serge was the uniform of my schooldays and to discard it was a symbol of my liberation.

"I won't promise," he said, "but it would be rather fun. The agéd or rather middle-agéd poet takes his bow in little Arthur's suit, after an enforced absence, owing to the pressure of no other engagements, of nigh on seventeen years. And yet . . . don't write this down as stage-fright . . . there is a risk. *Infandum renovare dolorem.* Nay, I shall promise you no promises. But mayhap, or more likely mayn'thap. Produce at least the vestment. Let us scrutinise it."

Even before I produced the vestment, I could see that Vickybird's mind was made up. "Superior cloth," he said, "the seat of the inexpressibles ever so slightly shiny, item the elbows; but well made, warm, durable."

"Hadn't you better try it on?" said his wife.

"What a wonderful woman I am married to!" he said. "Kiss me, ducky diamonds. She thinks of everything." He retired to the next room and reappeared in a few minutes, looking rather like the heroine of a Hollywood picture who having got drenched in a storm is wearing a suit of the hero's clothes. Kathleen and I burst out laughing. He minced round the room. "What I like about it," he said, "is it isn't too small!"

When we stopped laughing, he said, "In all gravity, M'sieur, 'dame, we have here enough, nay more than enough, for Vickybird's new rig-out. A little off the sleeves and trouser legs; the moving of a button or two on the twin-bosomed jacket. That surely, my darling whiff, is not a task beyond your skilful needle."

"I wouldn't touch it," she answered. "It's too broad on the shoulders and too large in the seat. Take it to the little tailor man and see if he can turn it and remake it to your shape."

"My turtle dove," he said, "your wisdom is only exceeded by your beauty. Tarry an instant, gentle sir, and we shall hie us to the local snip."

As he retired once more, his wife said, "I think he ought to go. It would do him good to get away from here, not to that Sanctuary of his, but where people really use their minds."

From the other room came Vickybird's voice:

"Oh, the next time I met her, I was dressed all in blue
All in blue! all in blue! We had a lovely do,
Down in the valley where she followed me."

The local tailor agreed to make over the suit for a pound or thirty shillings. Vickybird had his measurements taken, and then, still full of enthusiasm, suggested that we should walk on the Downs. "You have filled me, little Arthur," he said, "with a strange sense of elation, which though I cloak it with levity is more akin to levitation. What wouldst thou I should choose as the subject of my address to the assembled multitude?"

"Why not Blake's *Marriage of Heaven and Hell*?" I suggested.

"So be it! Amen," he said.

Later when we were sitting beside the dewpond close by Chanctonbury Ring, he told me of his break with Crowley. "You won't understand it," he warned. And he was quite right. It was partly because he took the ritual of Crowley's cult as much for granted as a Catholic takes the Mass. He felt no need to explain more than the barest detail.

One evening they were invoking Mars, and the ceremony started as usual with Crowley as the High Priest declaring, "The Temple is Open." There were the appropriate liturgies and invocations, and then Vickybird, who had been given a drug which he did not specify, rose to 'dance down' the God. 'Dancing down,' as I understood it, involved the abnegation of the dancer's own personality. He became a vacuum into which he drew the God.

Never in all the time that he was with Crowley, Vickybird said, had he been so successful. He was literally possessed by Mars. He was Mars.

"And then," said Vickybird, "instead of declaring that the Temple was closed, he deliberately dismissed us. He pretended later that it was forgetfulness. But he could no more forget that than a Catholic priest could forget the *Ite, missa est*."

"But if a Catholic priest did forget the *Ite, missa est*, would it matter very much?"

"Mars is the God of War, the God of killing," he said. "Don't you realise that when he dismissed us without closing the Temple he was sending not me, but the God Mars in me, loose on the streets of London."

"You're speaking figuratively."

"I'm speaking literally," he answered. "The first thing I remember was squeezing back into my soul. It was like being in a very small room with an immensely powerful man who wanted to kill me by sheer pressure. I told you that you wouldn't understand, and pray God that you never will. The God Mars is a killer and he wanted to use my body. I fought him for seventy-two hours before I gained possession of my body again."

"Did he kill anyone while he was in you?" I asked.

He dug a hole with his stick and buried the stub of my cigarette. "No," he said, "no, he didn't."

"Then I can't see what harm came of it all."

For a moment I thought he was going to answer. He opened his mouth to speak and then he looked at me as if seeing again my youth, and closed his lips. There had been something he had been going to say, but at the last moment he decided not to say it.

He got up. "So you see, little Arthur, I tell you why I broke away from The Beast and you still can't understand. But if you have any faith in a P.I.B. please don't have anything to do with him."

As we walked down through the beech wood with last year's leaves in places up to our calves, I remembered Auntie Helen's reference to 'The Tragedy' and her sudden silence. 'He will tell you when he wants to.' He wanted to, I thought, and yet he did not dare.

Vickybird was, as his wife said, 'a changed man;' but to my mind the change was for the worse. The lecture to the Poetry Society, dated some two months hence, became an obsession. "I have so much to tell the younger generation," he said. "Do you realise that I haven't given tongue since the year of Our Lord 1912?"

I tried gently to warn him that the meetings of the Poetry Society were *divertissements*, not memorial lectures; too much thought might cause more harm than too little. But the occasion, planted between the tropics of his imagination, grew with a monstrous speed. "On mature consideration," he announced, "I have decided that *The Marriage of Heaven and Hell* doesn't give me enough scope. I should like to hold forth on 'Poetry, Poesy and Ποίησις, or The Making, Mating and Matching of The Word.' "

"Out of the question," I said firmly; "we could never get it all on the Fixture Card. I'd far rather you talked on *The Marriage of Heaven and Hell*, but if you insist we can call it Poetry and Making, though from the point of view of our audience it would be far more sensible to talk about Poetry and Mating."

"Call it what you like on the Fixture Card," he said, "provided that you are resigned to the fact that I shall really be talking about The Making, Mating and Matching of The Word."

"Anyone would think from the way you talk," said his wife, "that no one had ever spoken to a bunch of undergraduates before."

"This is rather different," Vickybird rebuked quietly.

I didn't contradict him, because I knew that he was

quite right. Vickybird's lecture was going to be alarmingly different from any which we had had at the Poetry Society.

Every day he read me fresh extracts from his work in progress, strings of magic plays on words which became progressively more elaborate, like the coral reefs deposited by the Anthozoan polyps. When I returned to Oxford I received weekly progress reports and references to *der Tag*. "The snip has returned the suit," he wrote, "and it fits better than many I had from Savile Row. I shall not shame thee, little Arthur. For *der Tag* one should appear unobtrusively neat, if not disarmingly orthodox in dress, in view of the controversy The Paper will arouse."

Poor Vickybird! When the Day came he arrived as slashed and scarred as if he had been waylaid by a razor-gang. Waving like a flag a ream of exercise-book paper, he cried, "Poetry and Mating, an you will; but it shall be delivered with its full title."

It was without exception the worst lecture which we had at the Poetry Society. Vickybird delivered it with the conviction that it was an Open Sesame. Elusively allusive, it contained the peptonised wisdom of his lifetime without any of the roughage that his audience needed. His mystic shorthand was unintelligible. There was no discussion, because there was nothing to discuss; and the meeting broke up an hour earlier than usual.

I had feared that Vickybird would be mocked at; but this frost was something which I had never anticipated. I felt overwhelmed with guilt at having persuaded the little man to waste two months of his life preparing a fiasco and searched my mind for a formula of consolation. But everything I thought of seemed double-edged, calculated to rub salt into the wound it was meant to heal.

We reached the moonlit Broad without a word spoken. Outside the Sheldonian the shadows of the twelve Cæsars lay across the pavement as monstrous as they were in reputation. I took his arm. "Was it a terrible ordeal?" I asked.

"An ordeal!" he answered. "It was wonderful. What a glorious thing youth is and what an inspiration to address it! Did you notice how they hung upon my words? Their intent young faces fascinated! I am not, as you know, a conceited man, but I flatter myself that this evening I gave them something the like of which they never heard before. It was Good, you know." He stood in the middle of the Broad, a tiny figure in a blue serge suit, attended by a shadow of heroic stature. "This has convinced me, little Arthur. I have been too long in the wilderness. But the days of exile are drawing to their close. We shall return to the land flowing with milk and honey." He waved his lecture in a gesture which comprehended the twelve Cæsars, the Sheldonian Theatre, the arch of heaven and Blackwell's bookshop. "This is indeed Life!" he shouted and burst into a neigh of laughter which echoed down the street like a runaway horse.

I thought at the time that the last link of the slender chain which joined Vickybird to reality had snapped and his mind was moving into a new orbit within a private universe. And yet he seemed sane enough, filled with a new eagerness to face the world from which in the past he had sought every excuse to flee.

The Home of Lost Curses

In view of what I now know, I believe that despite all the pains he had taken with his lecture, what he said to us was of secondary importance. The true significance of that evening to him was, as he said, that it was his first public appearance for seventeen years, and that when it was over, the nightmare which had haunted him through the long years of exile did not become a reality. "The Tragedy" had not been mentioned.

When Vickybird went down from Cambridge, he immediately joined Crowley as his acolyte in the Temple and his assistant on the *Equinox*. It was Crowley who published Vickybird's first volume of poems, *The Triumph of Pan*, in the late autumn of 1910. Vickybird, to all intents and purposes, was Crowley's creature.

But in 1912 Crowley introduced a young girl into his circle. She was the wife of a well-known engraver, and though only twenty-one she had made something of a name for herself in Maeterlinck's *The Blue Bird*. She was very beautiful and very unhappy. It was probably her beauty that made Crowley interested in her, and her unhappiness that made her interested in magic. It offered an escape from life as she knew it.

Vickybird and Ione de Forrest, as she then called herself, fell passionately in love with one another. He provided, I imagine, the emotional balance which she needed. His temperament was as mercurial as hers, but even in the nadir of depression he believed in life; whereas she, despite her outbursts of gaiety, only really believed in death, the denial of being. Her solution to the problems of living was always in the last resort to kill herself. His sympathy and tenderness gave her reassurance and the courage to go on living.

She had a studio in Flood Street, Chelsea, and Vickybird took a place close by her. His passion inspired him, and every day he brought her new poems. Her husband instituted proceedings for divorce, and Vickybird asked her to marry him when the divorce had gone through. As a man and as a poet he was coming of age.

Crowley resented the affair because the devotion of the young poet and the young actress to him waned as their devotion to one another increased. It was the situation of the Dark Lady of the Sonnets over again, but Crowley had neither the spirit nor the poetical genius of Shakespeare. He was a vengeful man.

The happiness of Vickybird and Ione was not unclouded during the summer of 1912. In moments of depression she still talked of suicide; and in June she bought herself a pistol. Perhaps she bought it on the day when she discovered that she was pregnant.

Ione had a friend of her own age, Nina Hamnett, an artist of great talent but slender means, whom she used to take to the theatre and other entertainments, paying for them both out of the allowance which her husband made her and which he promised to continue after the divorce. She told Nina that she was with child, and when on the afternoon of Thursday, August 1st, she asked Nina to come round at eleven o'clock the next morning to Rossetti Studios to collect some clothes she wished to give her because she was going on a long journey, Nina decided that her friend intended to go somewhere abroad until the child was born.

Punctually at eleven Nina arrived at Ione's front door, to which was pinned an envelope addressed to her. Inside was the key of the door. Nina opened the door and went in, thinking that Ione had gone out for some reason.

In a sense she had. But her body was lying on her bed. Her bosom was bare and above the heart was a dark hole from which blood had flowed down on to the bedding. The pistol lay on the floor beside her and in the hearth was a heap of charred papers through which the occasional rustle of a draught was the only sound that broke the silence.

When a week later, at the inquest in the Chelsea coroner's court, Nina gave evidence, the words 'I am going on a long journey' took on a macabre significance, which Nina had not realised and which I believe Ione de Forrest had not intended; for the promise to give her clothes was consistent with a continued pregnancy but not with an intestate suicide. Between Thursday afternoon and Friday morning something happened which changed her mind.

Though this did not come out at the inquest, on the Thursday evening Vickybird and Ione had a violent quarrel. That was a thing that had happened before. Violent quarrels were followed by violent reconciliations. But on this occasion Vickybird at the height of the quarrel went to the door.

"If you go out of that door," Ione screamed, "I shall kill myself."

"All right," Vickybird answered. "Kill yourself then."

She had at last been given permission to do what she wanted. But, perhaps hoping that the permission would be revoked, she sat down and wrote two letters to be opened after her death, giving the impression that her suicide was due to quite other motives. Then in the hearth she made a bonfire of Vickybird's poems, letters and everything else which might incriminate him, listening maybe for his footsteps returning to her door.

But there was no sound. The last red spark died on the charred papers and she went slowly to the drawer where she kept her pistol.

Vickybird at twenty-three may have been a very different person from Vickybird at forty. But at no age can I imagine him in his senses flinging the cruel imperative 'kill yourself' at a girl he loved and wanted to marry, knowing that even when she was not pregnant she was obsessed with the idea of self-destruction. The only explanation is that he *was* out of his senses.

During the year 1912 there may have been two occasions when he was out of his senses. There was certainly the one he had told me about beside Chanctonbury dewpond, when Crowley deliberately failed to close the Temple and turned him loose upon the streets of London, possessed by the god of War. What the precise date was, Vickybird never told me. But the day of the week which Crowley would have chosen is certainly a Thursday, the day of the war-god Thor. And to my mind it is not too fanciful to imagine that the particular Thursday when Crowley committed the offence which Vickybird never forgave was August 1st.

Perhaps all that actually happened on that evening was that Vickybird returning from the Temple was possessed by aggressive instincts which he normally kept in control, and that to hear once again the stale threat of suicide was more than he could stand. But in his mind, I believe, the conviction existed that The Beast had planned the whole thing as a revenge against two of his disciples who had betrayed him.

If The Beast's aim had been revenge, it could scarcely have been more successful. The inquest was a most discreet affair. The husband was exonerated from all blame and a verdict of temporary insanity returned without any awkward investigation into the true motive. *The Times*, which in those days normally reported even the most obscure of suicides, omitted any reference to the case. The publicity was minimal and Vickybird's name was never mentioned.

But for him the absence of public censure was no consolation. He was left in his grief to face his guilt alone; to be his own executioner. He may himself have contemplated suicide, but his love of life was too strong for him to commit it. Instead he sentenced himself to a form of penal servitude, an infliction of the punishment that he felt he deserved.

To fortify this resolve, he built up the fantasy, which clearly had some foundation in fact, that though his name had never been mentioned publicly in the case, the inside story of the death of Ione de Forrest was common currency in Chelsea and Bloomsbury studios. Perhaps this was the reason for his retirement to the unlikely village of Steyning, and why when he published his poems from there, there was no mention of *The Triumph of Pan* or the author's name. This was the risk, he felt, even seventeen years later, in making a public appearance. He had served his sentence, but would people leave the past unburied?

That night in Oxford as he stood laughing in the Broad, he realised suddenly that a generation had grown up to whom Thursday, August 1st, 1912, was a forgotten day in childhood, not the unforgivable, never-to-be-forgotten moment when five harsh words uttered in a doorway blasted his life, ruined his ambitions and wrecked his peace of mind. It was the hysterical laughter of a prisoner who having sat for years in the confinement of his cell finds that the door of his prison is unlocked, has been unlocked maybe for years or always, and with a stride he steps out into the sunshine, free.

Chapter Eight

Matters of Grave Import

*

THE rift between my brother and myself began to close even before he left Oxford. When he went to Columbia University on a post-graduate course and I was in my last year at school, we began a correspondence which combined the pleasure of friendship with the intimacy of brotherhood. And for a few months on his return I had in his company a delight all the rarer because the old rivalries were ended.

He went back to the United States, this time in a very subordinate position in the G.E.C., Schenectady, at the same time that I went up to Oxford. Our correspondence was resumed, the four years difference in our ages now being not a barrier, but to me the most valuable of distinctions. He understood the things that worried me, and his advice was something I sought before using my own judgement.

Then, in the summer vacation of my second year at Oxford, my mother and I went to Belgium for three weeks. On the day of our return my father told us that my brother had been ill for a week. The next day he was dead.

What my parents suffered and the nature of their loss is clearer to me every year. At the time my own sorrow dwarfed everything. So many years had been spent running to catch him up that I could not imagine a future without the sight of him striding a quarter of a lap ahead. Now that his brief race was ended, full of promise but barren of achievement, the fancy grew in me that my own life would have no longer course than his. It remained with me until the day that I became older than he had been when he died, not a nightmare, but a quiet conviction of fatality.

In the four years that elapsed before then I stopped straining forward. At each stage I had been more precocious than he was. Now I explored deliberately the ground we had both surveyed, I from a distance and he from closer to. I had a half-formulated belief, not that my body had to make do for us both, but that if I re-experienced what he had experienced, I should, while remaining myself, become more what he would have become if he had lived. In deciding to be a writer, I believed that I had not only found my own *métier* but anticipated his. I was convinced that he would finally have become a novelist, in addition to or perhaps to the exclusion of being a scientist. But this may be an appreciation not of his genius but of his sympathy.

The Fitzroy Tavern in those days was the headquarters of most undergraduates with Bohemian tastes. I should inevitably have gone there in any case. But its appeal was deeper to me than to any of my friends, because of those nights I sat in my bedroom grinding out hexameters with the aid of a Latin Gradus, listening to the Fitzroy crowd moving to the Plough past my window, of the time I called out to my brother to stop, and the day-dreams I had when going to the Fitzroy was the symbol of manhood.

After my brother's death, though it may appear an improbable shrine, my visits to the Fitzroy Tavern were in the nature of a pilgrimage. *He* had stood at that horseshoe bar, beside the portrait of Kleinfeld by Augustus John. *He* had sat on the stuffed horsehair sofas, listening to Nina Hamnett talking about Gaudier and Modigliani. *He* had put pennies in the stridulent mechanical piano.

Occasionally I would ask people if they had ever met him, people I knew, from what he told me, he had met. "Oh, I remember," they would say. "He was a big chap with a beard, wasn't he?" or "Didn't he have red hair." His short trim figure, his blonde hair and white face, his light wit, had left no more impression on Fitzrovia than a bare foot on quicksand.

I enormously enjoyed evenings at the Fitzroy, the Marquis of Granby and the Plough, and the companionship of painters, writers and models older than myself. The illusion that I was at the centre of the intellectual and artistic tavern life of the great city was at first complete; then gradually it began to dawn on me that the painters and writers whom I met there were only part-time artists and their main occupation was drinking. Towards closing-time, becoming short of cash, they would draw on the capital of experience, and in return for a whisky or a pint of bitter, they would treat me to the cautionary tales of their careers, the moral of which always was, "For God's sake, don't make a habit of this place or you'll get no work done."

Betty May was an exception; for her there was no heart-searching, nor sense of failure. It was a life which she enjoyed enormously, and when she got bored with it she retired for a time or moved from one circle to another.

It was she who told me that Crowley had returned to London and was staying at the Eiffel Tower, not fifty yards from the Fitzroy. I begged her to introduce me. But she refused. "We're not on speaking terms," she said, "but if we were, I still wouldn't introduce you. That man is utterly evil."

That was the reason why I wanted to meet him. In a world where blacks and whites were breaking up so fast into various shades of grey, The Beast was the last of the graven images, an obsidian monolith of evil, a simple and reassuring devil. "If you ever got the chance to meet Crowley," I once asked my brother, "would you do it?" This was when I was fifteen.

"No," he said, after a time, "it would be too risky."

I sounded various people at the Fitzroy, and at last one, a young poet who at twenty-seven rightly considered himself a failure, promised he would try to arrange the meeting.

"But will he consent," I asked; "will he see a complete nobody like me?"

"He'll see anyone who'll see him," said the poet, "but watch out he doesn't land you with the bill."

The next day at lunch-time I was told that The Beast would see me at the Eiffel Tower that evening after dinner at nine o'clock.

"What d'you want to meet him for anyway?" asked the poet. "Isn't there enough trouble around without looking for it?"

This cynical attitude to evil seemed to me rather like blasphemy; but it brought home the realisation that I could not avow my real motive in coming to him, the desire to see what the Devil Incarnate looked like.

I had never dared to enter the Eiffel Tower, because it was reputed to be fabulously expensive. A meal for one person might cost anything from five shillings to seven and sixpence, which was a fortune in those days when you could have a four-course blow-out for half-a-crown.

I realised that The Beast would not be dining in full vestments; kilt and sporran would be hidden by the table-cloth, and if he had his five-foot wand with him he would probably have put it in the hat-and-cloak room. But I was sure a character as singular as The Beast's would stand out anywhere.

The small restaurant of the Eiffel Tower was almost empty. The only man sitting by himself was a bald and elderly stockbroker, apparently working out on the back of a menu calculations from the day's Closing Prices or the next day's form at Newmarket.

The waiters were playing dominoes at a table at the back. One of them looked round, laid his dominoes face down and donned a soupy jacket. "A table for one, sir?" he asked, as he came over.

"I was supposed to be meeting Mr Crowley," I said, "but it seems. . . ."

"There is Mr Crowley, sir," said the waiter, pointing to the stockbroker, who looked up at the mention of his name.

'One Must Not Judge by First Appearances,' I said to myself, as I went over to his table. And sure enough, he was not bald entirely. In certain parts his head was closely shaven; and elsewhere his hair had been allowed to grow slightly longer. These were the cabalistic tufts that Betty May had spoken of. They were, I thought, a shade too reticent to be fully effective; but perhaps it was a ritual modification for town wear.

"Do what thou wilt shall be the whole of the law," he remarked.

"Love is the law," I said in what I hoped was a casual voice, "love under Will."

He was a large, heavy man; and he sat down faster than he had got up. He had a paunch, I noticed. The waiter came over and stood by the table.

"I'm drinking Armagnac," The Beast said. "What would you like?"

"Armagnac would suit me fine," I said, drawing my chair forward so that I could see what The Beast had been writing on the back of the menu. I expected to see a series of hieroglyphs; but it was a shopping list with the figures of cost carefully noted against each item. "And why not?" I asked myself. "Even a magician has to make both ends meet. Don't be so romantic!"

The Beast handed me a knobbly cheroot and, remembering my father's maxim, "In an interview, let the other fellow start first. It puts him at a disadvantage," I took a long time to get it going to my satisfaction.

"Are you related to Robert Calder-Marshall of Shanghai?" he asked.

"He's my uncle," I said. "Have you been to Shanghai? Do you know him?"

"No," he said, "I was looking someone up in *Who's*

Who this morning and the name happened to catch my eye."

I wondered if the name for which the black magician who kept such neat accounts was looking had been my father's. And yet why shouldn't he? Every business man had a copy of *Who's Who*; so why not a magician?

The Beast's reputation so overawed me that I refused to accept the evidence of my eyes. In youth or middle manhood he might have looked remarkable, but the stamp of age had obliterated his individual pattern. He had the same dewlaps as actors who play corrupt senators in American films, a skin that was rough as a calf's tongue, a tired, used face, sagging with satiation.

The only thing that set him aside from others who have lived not wisely but too well was the upward twist, a conscious mephistophelian touch, which he had given to his eyebrows and which drew attention to his eyes. These must at some time have been powerful. I could imagine that the stories I had heard of his hypnotic powers had once been true.

"Why do you want to see me?" he asked.

"I am secretary of the Oxford University Poetry Society," I said. "I wanted to know whether you would come to Oxford next term to lecture."

He laughed. "You know perfectly well that they would never let me do it."

"That didn't seem to me any reason why you should refuse," I answered. "Unless of course you agreed with them."

"Agree?" he said, with a sudden change of manner. "Of course I don't agree. But a man in my position has

180

calumniators. Have you read this cheap, shoddy, lying nonsense that some Fleet Street fellow wrote for Betty May? That's the dirt that sticks."

"Why should we worry what the Authorities will say until they say it? After all, you and I aren't the Proctors."

Slowly his brain took in the suggestion. "That is perfectly true," he said. "This shall be a blow struck for Truth and Beauty. Yes, all right, I shall come and carry the war right into the enemy's camp."

I got out my diary and we fixed a date. The idea, once it had taken root, started to grow rapidly; and towards me his attitude, which had been distant, if not to say cagey, suddenly became expansive. "How did you come to be interested in magic?" he said.

I told him that I had known Vickybird for many years.

"Ugh, a weakling!" he said. "He had considerable gifts, but no stamina at all. I expect he's told you a lot of lies about me."

"He says that you have great magical powers," I answered, "but that you have consistently abused them."

"Bah!" he said. "He got mixed up in the suicide of some girl he'd put in the family way, and then he tried to blame the whole thing on to me. He's a neurotic; well, you've seen him." He stubbed out his cheroot. "You know, quite apart from this lecture, we ought to have a long talk sometime. Why not come down to my place in the country next vacation?"

"I'd like to," I said. "And by the way, we haven't fixed the subject of your lecture."

"What shall I talk about? Nothing too esoteric. What about Gilles de Rais? You ever heard of him?"

"Yes," I said, "and what *you* have to say about him would interest me very much."

When lecturers are asked to select their own subjects, most of them choose something which will enable them, however obliquely, to talk about themselves. This was why I was interested in Crowley's choice of the young Marshal of France. The life of Gilles de Rais might in Crowley's eyes be a monstrous skiograph of his own career. Perhaps the thirty thousand pounds which he had inherited in youth from Crowley's Ales was comparable to the vast estates which came to the young Gilles from Jeanne de Rais and Marie de Craon. The period of soldiering with Jeanne d'Arc was paralleled by the assault on Kanchenjunga. The young Marshal became a mystical writer and a patron of the arts, who to meet the liabilities of his generosity was driven to alienate his lands and sell estates. Like Crowley, he had run through his patrimony by an early age.

To redeem his fortunes Gilles turned from mysticism to alchemy and necromancy, in the same way that Vickybird said that Crowley foreswore the true discipline of the unworldly Macgregor Mathers to make money and indulge his own senses.

In the personality of Gilles de Rais there seemed an interesting split. The more he spent on the cultivation of the black arts, the more extravagant he became in his charity and the celebration of the rites of the Christian Church. Perhaps it was a cloak. Perhaps he thought he could buy the indulgence of the clergy. Or was he trying to drive a bargain with God as well as the Devil?

That was a question which I wanted to hear The Beast answer, for the light it would throw on his own attitude to Christianity. I suspected that, for all his talk of Magic, Crowley had come to primitive magic through the worship of the Christian Devil. "You know perfectly well they'd never let me do it" was, I imagined, more than a statement of fact; it was an acceptance of Christian values as implicit as a thief's acceptance of the laws of property.

At his trial Gilles de Rais was accused of kidnapping a hundred and forty victims, mostly boys, and of torturing them. He was a powerful landowner in an age when the Lord of the Manor was the minister of the central laws. But even so, it is hard to believe that a terror so extensive could have passed for so long unpunished. From The Beast's explanation I hoped to find some clue to the mysterious deaths met by Crowley's own followers.

At the beginning of term the Proctors receive the Fixture Cards of all University Societies; and rather to my surprise no objection was raised to the name of Aleister Crowley or the subject of his lecture. "Perhaps," I said to Hugh, "they're getting wise and realise the way to explode a myth is to exhibit the reality."

I was wrong. The lecture was banned a few days before Crowley was due to speak. The Proctors were just slow readers.

Immediately telegrams flew backwards and forwards between ourselves and Crowley, who was all set to strike his blows for Truth and Beauty. "Protest Scandalous Violation of Civil Liberties," he wired wildly, "Banning Slanderous Aspersion on Moral Character."

We discussed the possibility of hiring the private room at the Spreadeagle, Thame, and chartering a beastly fleet of buses. Hugh reported that John Fothergill was ready for anything barring a Black Mass. But the Proctors intimated that even if the meeting was held outside Oxford, it would be raided and anybody attending would be liable to be sent down.

"Demand Lecture be Printed Sold Streets Oxford," The Beast roared back. "Else Legal Action stop Text in Post."

Hugh was delighted. "This should be bigger than the Balloon Story."

Together we went to the offices of the *Oxford Mail* and interviewed Charles Fenby. "Give me an exclusive on the Banned Lecture story," Fenby said, "and I'll have five hundred copies of the lecture on the streets within twenty-four hours of getting copy."

The lecture arrived first post the next morning. I began it eagerly, and as soon as I had succeeded in finishing it, I went round to the *Oxford Mail*.

"You don't expect me to print this trash," Fenby said. "Any hack in Fleet Street could do better than this in half an hour on a pint of bitter."

"That's the lecture you promised to print," I said.

"But this stupid, hypocritical nonsense!" Fenby said, hitting the manuscript with annoyance. "Crowley must be mad."

"Perhaps he wrote it especially for the Proctors," I suggested, "to prove that he's not the sinister old beast, but a silly old fool."

"All right," Fenby said. "I'll publish the bloody thing,

as I promised to. But next time you come to me with a proposition, there'll be no strings attached."

Whether the publication of the Banned Lecture raised Crowley's stock with the Proctors is doubtful; it certainly deprived him of any sympathy he had won with under-graduates at being banned. About fifty copies were sold before word got round that it was trash; then sales dropped dead.

But The Beast was exultant. "You have done great work for me," he wrote. "Let me know when you want to come to my place at Knockholt and I will send you full directions. There are Matters of Grave Import we should discuss together. . . ."

We had driven through the purlieus of south-east Lon-don, skidding in tramlines, nosing between the kerb and trams, trying to ignore the infiltration of rain through the weak spots in roof and windscreen, and had emerged in bleak sunlight into the dank fields of north Kent.

"The next place we come to according to this map is Knockholt," I said.

"I don't know why we're going to see this Black Magician, do you?" Eleanor asked. "A cinema would have been warmer, and probably funnier."

I pointed to a desolate platform. "That must be Knockholt Station," I said.

"That must be why they've written up KNOCKHOLT STATION," she said. "Now where does this warlock live?"

I pulled out his letter. " 'The cottage, which is very charming, is rather off the beaten track.' Ah, here we are!

'Approaching from the Station, take the first to the left' . . ."

When we reached the very charming cottage, it was clear that The Beast had rented the week-end residence of some spinster of moderate means and ghastly good taste at a nominal rent for the off-season. He cut a strange figure against copper warming-pans, ships-in-bottles, a Cosy Stove and comfy cretonne-covered armchairs.

The Beast opened the door to us, holding in his left hand a palette and brushes. What pleasure he had at seeing me was overlaid by his surprise at the presence of Eleanor. "Where are your bags?" he asked.

"We have no bags."

"But you are staying two or three days, surely," he said.

"It was never even mentioned," I answered; "we're dining in London."

He clicked his tongue in annoyance. "I took it for granted," he said. For a moment he stood in the doorway as if it weren't worth our while to cross the threshold except for a protracted session. Then he went into the living-room, leaving us to follow. By the time I had joined him, he had opened the door on to a winding oak staircase and was calling up in a tongue I did not understand. He closed the door and scowling slightly waved his palette at Eleanor. "I am painting," he said. "Trance-states."

Round the walls, between the horse-brasses, hung a number of livid canvases, which despite their lack of design gave off a sullen aura. He picked up the picture on which he had been working. It looked like a pair of buttocks one of which had been flayed and the other beaten with hose-pipe. "You've never seen anything like this before," he said; "it amazes *me*."

The room above was separated only by oak boards laid over beams, and in our room it sounded as if a fawn was trotting backwards and forwards over our heads.

The Beast began rummaging among a pile of canvases stacked in a dark passage. He lugged them out, held them up in the half-light for an instant and then returned them to their precious obscurity. "This is what Blake was striving for," he said simply.

From the noise above it was clear that the fawn was trying to come down the staircase, but finding it difficult. Eleanor and I looked at one another, prepared for the appearance of almost any familiar. The door creaked open and on the bottom stair for a moment, framed in the doorway like a full-length picture, stood one of the most remarkable women that I have ever seen. She wore a black-and-white satin dress, which lubriciously emphasised the exuberance of her hips and bust. Its singular *chic* brought into the living-room of that furnished cottage during the off-season the brilliance of Rio de Janeiro in the sunlight, the colour and *ton* of the Avenida Rio Branco or the Rua do Ovidor in the high season. Black open-work stockings and tapering four-inch heels gave the illusion of slenderness and length to typically South American Indian legs.

"My wife!" said The Beast. "She is a Brazilian, but she has a little English."

"'Ow are you?" asked The Beast's wife, investing the

three words of welcome with unclubbable aloofness. She held out a plump white hand whose stubby fingers had been lengthened by cultured talons, lacquered the red of venous blood.

"What a pity you aren't staying overnight," said The Beast. "My wife is a magnificent cook—in the Brazilian manner."

"Really!" I could not believe that the art and labour which had gone to the preparation of her appearance could be diverted to dressing food. She did not look a kitchen-body.

Even in Brazil she would have seemed exotic, but in Knockholt in December she was fantastic. Her hair, like many an Indian woman's, was fine, black, straight and glossy, growing with such luxuriance that her face was like a small clearing in a jungle only prevented from reverting to secondary scrub by intensive cultivation. Her pupils were dark and large by nature. By the use of kohl upon her eyelids, and the beading of her long lashes with mascara, she had produced an effect which would have been magnificent on a map twice the size of hers. As it was, the enlargement emphasised the struggle which each of her features had for *Lebensraum*. Nature had found room only for thin short lips, but over them she had painted a generous cupid's bow in carmine.

In consequence her nose, in itself regular and proportionate to her natural features, appeared almost desperate in its struggle to survive.

Standing by Eleanor with her long, clean body, her finely cut and scarcely made-up features, she was like one of the extravagant dolls which tarts keep on their beds and suburban women on the cottage-grand piano.

I turned back to the Lover of Truth and Beauty standing flanked by trance-states. His ventral muscles, like perishing elastic, were sagging worse than ever.

"Calder-Marshall and I have matters to discuss," he said to his wife. "Put some water on to boil for tea." Then he turned to Eleanor. "Now that it has turned fine, I expect you would like my wife to show you round the estate."

Eleanor looked bleakly through the cottage window at a garden patch on which the winter sun shone without conviction, at the yellowing Brussels sprouts, the rain-soaked broccoli and the mud.

"Moment," said the Brazilian. "I change my shoes, yes."

The four-inch heels clattered up the stairs and over our heads.

"Is the estate *very* large?" asked Eleanor.

"You can walk for miles," said The Beast brightly. "It isn't mine, of course."

The heels clattered down the stairs again, but this time they were five inches in height. "Is better, yes?" she asked Eleanor.

As soon as he had sent the women out, The Beast locked the door. Then he went to a cupboard and took out two glasses and a bottle of brandy. "This is better than tea," he said, setting them on a table and pointing to a chair. "I'm sorry you brought that girl down. One can't talk seriously with women around." He poured two stiff brandies and handed me what looked like two inches of coarse grass doubled over at each end.

"What do I do with this?" I asked.

"Brazilian cigarette," he said. "Purest tobacco in the world."

It certainly had the highest nicotine content. As I sucked the dry maize husk desperately to keep it alight, a repulsive stream oozed on to my lips and fingers.

"Drink up," he said.

I drank up, and he poured two more brandies. "I was pleased at the way you handled that lecture," he said; "you have great possibilities. You know nothing, of course, but at your age that doesn't matter. That will come with time and study and experience. Have you any money of your own?"

"No."

"And your parents wouldn't make you any allowance?"

"Certainly not."

"It's a pity, of course. But it's not an insuperable difficulty. Money can always be found." He leaned forward with his elbows on the table. "What do you intend to do when you come down from Oxford?"

"I'm going to write."

"But if you have no money and your father won't make you an allowance," he said, "how are you going to live?"

"I don't know."

"I could give you work while you were learning to write," he said. He leaned forwards with his elbows on the table with even more than the fixity which I had noticed at the Eiffel Tower. I suddenly realised, not that he had once had hypnotic powers, but that in this furnished room in Knockholt, having sent the women out into the vegetable garden, he was trying as quickly as possible to hypnotise *me*.

"Have another brandy," he said, raising the bottle without looking away from me and filling my glass but not his.

I drew my chair in to the table and leaned forward on my elbows gradually so that our eyes were only about a foot apart. His, weak and rather rheumy, were trying desperately to shine, like the bulb of a torch whose battery is failing.

I had cherished the idea of a devil incarnate for six years as a relic of childhood and it had stood up to every test except meeting The Beast himself. His shoddy fight for 'Truth and Beauty', his trashy lecture, his arrogant, inferior painting, and now this attempt to hypnotise me with the aid of brandy produced a revulsion in me against the childishness which I had pampered all these years. When I came down to it, all it amounted to was this shagged and sorry old gentleman, trying to outstare me across a table.

"It's very kind of you," I said. "Is this an offer of employment?"

"Would you like to work with me?" he asked.

"There is only one thing I want to do and that is to write well," I said. "You have been practising magic for a long time. But your movement has produced no literature."

It was a strange conversation because, though it was all above board, it existed on three levels. The ground floor was the table on which our glasses and the brandy stood. The first floor was our verbal conversation, and the attic was this queer, visual contest, like two animals trying to stare each other into submission.

"You have read my works?" he said.

"I have," I said; "they may be wonderful as magic, but I can't believe that anything which is so badly written could be."

He showed no more anger than when Betty May poured the bowl of water over his head at Cefalu. "Why don't you stay the night?" he said. "You can tell that girl of yours to go home by herself."

I found that instinctively I was being more and more rude to The Beast before I realised that for all these years I had been looking for Milton's idea of Satan, a figure of Pure Evil; and that this impure character, trying rheumily to hypnotise me, was the genuine article. Evil was never Pure. I began to let myself go.

The brandy with which he plied me at a remarkable speed provided me with the fire and the justification for attack. But he did not mind. "You are really interested in magic," he said, "but you are frightened. That is why you are saying these things. I've heard it so often. Why don't you just stay till tomorrow morning? There's such a lot to talk about. And there's plenty of brandy."

A handful of hail struck the window, and in a moment there was a rattling at the back-door. "Shouldn't you open the door?" I said.

The Beast continued to look me in the eyes, but he threw the doorkey on the table. "You do it," he said. "You're young. You can do anything, eh?"

I took the key. But I didn't get up. It was more difficult than I had expected. "My offer still stands," The Beast said. "I don't mind how rude people are provided that they say what they think. Why not stay the night?"

I got up and went to the back-door. As I fumbled getting the key in the lock, I said to him, "You don't know how grateful I am for your entertainment." I opened the door as the rain came pouring down. La Senhora and Eleanor tumbled into the room.

"What on earth have you been doing all this time?" Eleanor said.

I looked across at the old man bent over the table with the brandy bottle at his elbow. He was scowling as much at me as at Eleanor. "What would you say we have been doing, sir?" I asked.

"I'd say I'd been wasting my time," he said, and he picked up the brandy bottle and carried it to the cupboard.

"But at least, sir," I said, "I must thank you for saving a great deal of mine."

Chapter Nine

The Voices of Experience

*

WHEN Hugh proposed that we should listen to the voices of experience, I was more amused than anything. It had become a hobby to see just how far he would go and in what direction. But after the session at Knockholt I was seized with a minor panic. I had met The Beast and the mask of Evil was broken. I didn't care tuppence whether he had celebrated the death of Adonis in Cefalu in 1923, or deliberately possessed Vickybird with Mars in 1912. In December 1929 he was, as far as I was concerned, little better than a pedlar of spells as phony as quack medicines.

On the other hand, he had offered me a job, to get me started as a writer. What I should do for a living when I went down was becoming an urgent question. Hugh's preoccupation with making useful contacts, which I had dismissed as 'common Hughdness,' had more to it than I had realised at the time. A lot of what I had regarded as villainy and calculation in him was merely common sense.

I tried to think back over the year when we had been listening to the voices of experience. What had I learnt? I had learnt first that almost no writer whom we thought was any good was prepared to come to the Oxford Poetry Society in return for first-class train fare and board and lodging in order to speak to a bunch of undergraduates.

Roy Campbell, D. H. Lawrence and Ezra Pound were excused because they were abroad. Robert Bridges was excused because he was over eighty, and he wasn't a very good poet either. The address of Wyndham Lewis, for whom I had a tremendous admiration, was unknown. He was excused. Virginia Woolf had made a vow never to speak again in public, because it made her ill. T. S. Eliot was too busy helping Mr Faber and Mr Faber. Siegfried Sassoon was working; Robert Graves refused to address any Poetry Society at which Humbert Wolfe had spoken, because it showed we couldn't distinguish between Poetry and Verse (anyway he was in Mallorca). Aldous Huxley could not possibly regard himself as a poet on the strength of *Leda* and the poems scattered through his novels.

The only great artist who had the time and kindness to talk to us was Walter de la Mare. I could not remember a single phrase of his (as I remembered for example Alan Porter's description of John Donne's method of writing as "a five-sense alembification through the intellect"), yet even to this day I retain a vivid impression of that evening. He succeeded in doing what Vickybird strove to do when he talked of Poetry and Making. Since then I have met two other people who had the same magic in talking to an audience, James Stephens and Algernon Blackwood. Both of them could make an audience wait on words and listen spellbound. De la Mare did something more remarkable that evening. He held us spellbound in explaining how to bind spells; and though he was talking about writing poetry, what he said was equally true of prose, the balance between technique and vision. This creation of a magic out of creating magic has remained with me longer than anything else which I heard at the Poetry Society, and I hope that Walter de la Mare will feel that the evening which he spent, in return for board, lodging and a return rail-fare, wasn't wasted.

One of the friendliest of the visiting lecturers was the erudite Willson Disher, who spoke on the subject of the famous Victorian equestrienne Ada Isaacs Mencken. The connection between Ada Isaacs Mencken and poetry was tenuous, but in the later days of the Poetry Society, the original aims were forgotten. It was true that at one period of her life this strapping Amazon was wooed by the diminutive Algernon Charles Swinburne; he is even said to have proposed marriage, sitting on her knee. But the idyll was brief. A photograph appeared for sale on the streets of London, showing the darling of the circus seated in full riding-kit with the poet standing by her side. Even so the top of the great poet's head reached only to her ear; and the equestrienne was forced to deny him her presence because his devotion was making her ridiculous.

Willson Disher was so amusing that I invited him to lunch the next day. In the middle of the third bottle of Beaune he looked up grinning and said, "You chaps don't realise how lucky you are in this place, meeting all the nobs and what not. I do envy you, really. Make the most of it while it lasts."

His words were like a January wind blowing through the open door of a hot house. "It isn't as wonderful as all that," I said.

"Oh yes it is," he answered. "I know. I never had it."

We cast our net wider and wider. A daily newspaper, in emulation of the celebrated Cholmondeley (Chum) Frink of *Babbitt*, had signed up a poetess called Wilhelmina Stitch. Six days a week in a box appeared her Fragrant Minute, printed as prose but with rhymes which popped up perkily at regular intervals. This device made the best of both worlds. It recognised the public's hatred of poetry and the sense of shame that people felt at being seen reading it. Yet at the same time it gave them the satisfaction, furtively, of discovering where one line ended and another began. "We must at all costs get Wilhelmina Stitch," Hugh said. "What a scoop!"

"We'll never get her," I said. "She'll be far too leery. She's probably a man anyway."

I was wrong. Wilhelmina Stitch was a woman and she was far too leery to refuse.

She knew that we were out to rag her, but she was confident that she, a mother, with children our age, could hold her own. She came from the North Country, a tiny, sallow-faced, mousy-haired woman who had learned that her strength lay in exploiting her weakness. Stitch was her maiden name but she clung to it in her work. Wilhelmina Stitch! It was a combination so absurd that no one could forget it; yet at the same time it was not high-falutin, it was extraordinarily ordinary. It conjured up an image of dowdy worthiness, which her person and her poems reinforced. She was all of a piece. The only glimpse she gave of an *alter ego* was one moment at the end of dinner, when missing what I thought had been a collar of white rabbit's fur from her neck, she exclaimed in sudden fear, "Where's my ermine?"

Over dinner she made one essay into poetic small-talk. Looking dreamily out of the windows of the Randolph at the trees growing in the churchyard beside the Martyrs' Memorial, she remarked, "Don't you love it when the chestnut trees in spring take off their woolly gloves and stretch their baby fingers?" This seemed to me to open up an area of discourse for whose exploration one could find no better guide than the author of Fragrant Minutes. But unfortunately Stephen Spender, in the midst of swallowing clear soup, was caught by a paroxysm which returned it through the nose. Miss Stitch stopped short in the middle of a fancy about the chestnuts lighting up their little candles for the birthday of the May Queen, and there was an uneasy silence which remained unbroken, until Hugh bent forward and asked her whether she was an admirer of the works of her fellow poetess, Edith Sitwell.

"*I* like them very much," she answered; "they are of course caviare to the multitude. She is my neighbour, you know, in Moscow Road. I often see her." Then with a tinge of sadness in her voice, she added, "I sometimes think it a pity that she doesn't realise that while her poems may bring joy to a few hundred choice spirits like you and I, mine bring hope and heartsease to millions of poor people who have no other poetry in their lives. Some people think that the Fragrant Minute is just a job like any other. But if you read those sad, sad letters I receive in thousands every week, you'd realise that it was something far, far more, something . . . well . . . if you must have it . . . more like a Sacred Trust."

This was a rehearsal, I realised later, when after paying the bill for the Treasurer I was squatting in a crowded room. If we had lapped up the chestnuts taking off their woolly gloves, our members would have been treated to the exhibition of Stitchcraft they desired. As it was, she was forewarned, defensive and skilfully apologetic.

Sinclair Lewis let Babbitt overhear the drunken Chum Frink weeping and moaning that if he hadn't prostituted himself he might have been a decent poet. I could detect no such conflict in Wilhelmina Stitch. Any doubts that she might have had at the outset had been allayed by fan-mail and the crowded meetings she addressed in mining and industrial areas, wherever in fact the present was so drab and the future so uncertain that people welcomed any anodyne, from betting to red biddy. The Fragrant Minute was a palliative, maybe; but it was cheaper and less noxious than most. She was touched (as, if it happened with *their* work, many greater poets would be touched) by horny-handed men carrying clippings of her Fragrant Minutes in their work-cards, and care-worn housewives sticking them between the Woolworth mirror and its frame.

The knowledge that she had a mass following made her secure against the contempt of highbrows; or almost secure. If she had felt as confident as she sounded that evening, there would have been no need for her to accept the invitation.

Starting with a hostile audience (and there is no audience initially more cruel than that of Oxford or Cambridge undergraduates), she won them round with stories of people who wrote to her and who through their letters often gave her the ideas for Fragrant Minutes. Her poems might be bad, her philosophy sentimental, but the material on which they worked was the genuine stuff of life; not intellectual abstractions but everyday worries, apparently insoluble problems, moments of joy which shot like shafts of sunlight into the clouded lives of the majority of the English people of that time. We, her audience of that night, as she made us realise, were a privileged minority, whose values might appear to us absolute but were to most people, living near the hunger line, remote, unrealistic and rather absurd.

She was so tactful in her approach, criticising us not directly but by implication, that she succeeded in winning the sympathy of most of her audience before she read a line of her verse. By the time that she picked up a collected volume of her Fragrant Minutes, all accepted standards of judgment had been swept aside. Standing behind her, daring us to laugh or criticise, stood the invisible hordes of the sick, the mutilated, the unemployed and the overworked who were, she had almost induced us to believe, restrained from committing mass suicide only by reading the Fragrant Minute.

"Do, Miss Stitch, please," a young man begged, "do read that poem of yours called The Page Boy. It really is quite the most suggestive poem I've ever read."

There was a gust of laughter, a sense of relief that someone dared to crack one of the old undergraduate jokes.

But Miss Stitch neither smiled nor looked angry. She waited for the laughter to subside and then, with a brightness full of innocence, she said, "I'm glad you like that one. It is the one the Lancashire miners love best."

Miss Stitch that evening more than held her own. She

triumphed as Horatio Bottomley had triumphed in the Union, when he disarmed criticism by saying that the only university he had attended had been the University of Life. But why she decided to speak to a hostile audience in Oxford when there were so many places where she was received with enthusiasm remained a mystery till a few years later, when I found if not the answer at least an important clue. Drinking in the Fitzroy Tavern, I fell into conversation with a sallow-faced young man with shining black hair. I enjoyed intellectual chit-chat more then than I do now, and didn't resent being called a highbrow. But the conversation of this young man was altogether too rarefied for my taste. Seeing a friend come in, I went over to him.

"Who is that chap I was talking to?" I asked.

"He's a nice fellow, really," my friend said, "but he's touchy. He's Wilhelmina Stitch's son; and if you mention the Fragrant Minute, he sees red."

"Is it conceivable," I wondered, "that just as we her audience saw massed behind her the myriads of the miserable, Wilhelmina Stitch saw in us so many derisive children who had to be convinced that what she was doing was a matter not for shame but pride?"

The Voices of Experience had taught me very little that was of immediate practical use. Somehow or other people managed to survive as writers; but how *I* could survive was quite a different question. I had edited the *Oxford Outlook*. I had written a few short stories which had been printed on the back page of the *Manchester Guardian*. But frankly I had no qualifications for any job.

I went round to the editors of the different weeklies. Edmund Blunden was sitting at the literary editor's desk in the *Nation* office. "You couldn't have come down from the University at a worse time," he said; "the depression is just striking us. How much longer the *Nation* will be able to carry on I just don't know."

Perhaps there was a time when young men coming down from a University were welcomed in London literary circles with open arms. But the grave warnings I received from Blunden, Robert Lynd, Raymond Mortimer and Hayter Preston were true not only of the year that I left Oxford, but of every year since. Without capital there was no means of making a start.

"If you want to be a novelist," my father said, "wouldn't it be best to write a novel?"

This had never occurred to me. "But how could I live while I'm writing it?"

"How long does writing a novel take?" he asked.

"I don't know," I said, "but an awfully long time. About a year, I think."

"And how much would you get for it?"

"Twenty-five pounds; or with luck fifty."

"You'd better wipe that out as a career then," he said.

"Maybe I could write a novel in six months," I suggested.

"I'll continue your allowance for three months," he answered. "If you write a thousand words a day, you'll finish it in two months, and then you can spend the last month typing and revising it."

My mother and I went to live in Bonn, while I wrote the novel at the rate of a thousand words a day. I had never imagined that it could be so difficult to describe people, to move them in and out of rooms, to condense their conversations. I discovered the significance of punctuation, inversions, ellipses. The language which I had used without thought for twenty-one years suddenly became a matter for wonder, discovery and experiment. While Stephen Spender, who had joined us, sat in his upstairs room in my mother's superb phrase 'dilettanteing with his typewriter, as usual,' I sat writing and re-writing, bewildered by the richness of the language in which I had chosen to work. Where there were so many different ways of expressing any thought, it seemed impossible to discover which was best.

But I returned to London with the typescript of a seventy-thousand-word novel in my suitcase. I had written a book, and my father, reading it through, pronounced that it wasn't bad for a first effort. It was submitted to Elkin Mathews, because I had a letter of introduction to a partner in that firm.

The moment I had put it in the post, I went back and read through the carbon. I had been working three months in a dream, thinking each day of how many words I had written and whether it would be finished in time. Now that it had gone to a publisher, I was able to read it as a whole, with some of the objectivity of a publisher's reader. It was terrible.

Every day I went to the British Museum and read the plays of Ben Jonson in the first edition, making notes on his spelling and punctuation. I pretended to myself that I was embarking on a work of scholarship which would bring me in ten or twenty years' time the acclaim of the academic world. But I knew secretly that I was trying to distract my mind from the knowledge that the book would be rejected. It was like awaiting the results of an examination which I knew that I had failed but my parents were confident that I had passed.

The rejection came in the form of a letter saying that Elkin Mathews regretted that they could not publish this novel, but would be interested to see any further work I did.

"I think that's very encouraging," said my mother.

"Who are you going to send it to next?" asked my father.

"I'm not," I said. "I'm going to tear it up. It isn't any good."

"Isn't that rather silly," my father said, "when you've put three months' hard work into that book?"

But I knew that the three months' hard work were not in the book, but in my own brain. I knew where to put commas now, and how to avoid the use of adverbs describing tones of voice, and indicate a pause without saying, 'Then there was a pause.' I knew how to quicken narrative and how to slow it down, how to imply meanings without stating them. The book wasn't a novel at all, it was an exercise book; and there was no need to keep it, because I knew all those lessons by heart.

I couldn't explain all this to my parents, because to them the symbol of success was the printed volume. From their point of view I had let them down doubly by throwing it on one side after its first rejection. I spent the morning in the Museum with Ben Jonson. But I didn't look at him. I was analysing my failure. One night in

Bonn, Ernst Robert Curtius, in the middle of discussing the book I was writing, had said, "You know, it seems funny I should be talking about this novel of yours when it is obvious that you will write nothing which I should want to read until you're fifteen or twenty years older." There were only two things holding me back in my career. The first was that I didn't know how to write, and the second was that I had nothing to write about.

At half-past twelve I left the Museum and made my way to Bertorelli's in Charlotte Street. As I passed beneath our old flat in Bedford Court Mansions I reflected that when I had lived there my dearest wish had been to be twenty, not fifteen; and now that I was twenty-one, I was longing to be thirty-five.

I went into the upstairs dining-room and took a table in the window looking out over Windmill Street and the Fitzroy Tavern. There went Nina Hamnett, with her long thin legs and her cloche hat, streaking like a busy emu from the Fitzroy to the Marquis of Granby. And there from the Marquis of Granby emerged a group of undergraduates with Betty May at their hilarious centre. Slowly they walked across Charlotte Street and disappeared into the Fitzroy Tavern.

"Hello. How's things?"

I looked up into the bland, shining face of Willson Disher.

"You expecting someone?" he asked, "or can I join you?"

I said that I would love him to join me, but that I would not be very good company.

He sat down and ordered his meal, then asked me what

was wrong. As I started with the self-importance of youth to lay my whole story before him, the wine waiter came up. "I can't run to a Beaune like you gave me on your Dad that day," he said. "But what about a spot of Beaujolais, on me?"

In the middle of a third bottle of Beaujolais, having listened with stoical forbearance to every detail, relevant or irrelevant, Disher said, "You can always be a schoolmaster, yer know. Good long holidays."

"But it would be hell," I objected.

"There's a lot to be said for hell, if you're going to be a novelist," Disher answered. "So much more goes on there."

"That's perfectly true," I said in a fit of illumination, "and in a way, the worse the school, the better. I wonder if there's anything going at Narkover."

"The place to go," Disher said, "is Gabbitas & Thring. I believe it's incredible some of the jobs they have there."

In the field of scholastic appointments Gabbitas & Thring are as famous as Gilbert and Sullivan, May and Baker or Romulus and Remus in their respective spheres. As Bertorelli's closed, we finished the dregs of the Beaujolais, I wrung Disher by the hand and, for fear that the mood of determination might otherwise evaporate, hailed a passing taxi.

In the cab, and later in the outer office of Gabbitas & Thring, while waiting for my interview, I elaborated the significance of the step I was taking. Wilhelmina Stitch had been right in her implied criticisms. University standards might appear absolute in the academic world, but they were incredibly remote from the hurly-burly of the novelist's world. Fitzrovia which I had considered in some way a counterbalance was really just as parochial and far more depressing. Contact with life in the raw was what I needed; and was life ever rawer than in a school? My future, which that morning had been confused and overcast, appeared startlingly clear as I was shown into the office of Mr Gabbitas, Mr Thring or their representative.

As he took down my particulars, he appraised my points with a rapidity I had noticed previously only in cattle-fanciers but which I realise now to be the common expertise of all dealers in commodities which change hands most often when they are unsatisfactory. "And what can I do for you?" he said at last.

"I've come to the conclusion that I have been over-educated," I said. "I want to declass myself. I should like a job in the worst school you have on your books."

Experienced though he obviously was in the detection of defrocked priests, paederastic scoutmasters and secret drinkers, he seemed for a moment taken aback. "We have only good schools on our books," he said.

"But some are surely better than others."

"That is perfectly correct."

"Well, I want one that isn't, if you understand me."

I thought that I detected behind his spectacles a glint of approval at the restatement of my requirements. "Of course," he said, "you could scarcely have come at a worse time, since most schools reassemble this week or next. But it so happens that one of our clients, a Mr Crump, broke his leg yesterday, playing football. Mr Crump will not be able to take up his position as Senior Classics

Master at Bogglesham Grammar School until mid-term;
and so there is a temporary vacancy for six weeks at a
salary rather higher than Burnham Scale. Bogglesham
Grammar School is now represented on the Headmasters'
Conference, so that it ranks as a Public School. But I
think it might be exactly what you're looking for. Why
don't you go down to see the Headmaster tomorrow?"

"It sounds very promising," I said. "There was an old
Bcoggleshamian at my college who always called the
Ballet 'the Bolly!'"

Bogglesham Grammar School was a gracious seven-
teenth-century red-brick building situated in the middle
of the hamlet of Bogglesham, immediately opposite a
genuinely Tudor Inn, which had Bass on draught. Fifty
or even twenty years before, the school had catered for
the children of the neighbourhood, sons of farmers, shopkeepers and farm workers. But the enterprise of the railway company laid Bogglesham open to the invasion of the
lower-paid office workers from the great City. Their
semi-detached residences surrounded and almost obliterated the village, and the influx of their sons had elevated
the modest grammar school to the dignity of being represented at the Headmasters' Conference.

The door was opened to me by the Headmaster, a man
so ecclesiastical in manner that his collar and tie appeared
to be mufti. He shook my hand and adroitly side-stepped
to allow two screaming boys to dash past him into the
playground squirting ink at one another with water-
pistols. "My boys," he called, "please to moderate the
hubbub."

They took not the slightest notice, but as they turned the corner of the building, the uproar died down till it sounded more like a distant street riot. "My two youngest!" he said. "Splendid boys, both!"

My first impression could not have been more favourable and I rather liked the way, when we were sitting in his study, the Headmaster implied that Mr Crump had broken his leg deliberately in order to cripple Bogglesham Grammar School with the expense of getting a temporary master. "As if he couldn't have done it before Christmas," he said, "so that I could have chosen a really good man, instead of having to buy a pig in a poke." The voices of both the splendid boys returned and the hooves galloped past the study door and up the stairs. For a moment the Headmaster frowned and I thought that he intended to administer some gentle reproof, but then, apparently realising its futility, he shook his head. "Now— where was I? Oh, yes. A great big happy family, that's it. That's how I like to think of Bogglesham; just one great big happy family; and if you come to Bogglesham, any of the masters will tell you just the same." There was a loud thud and the merriest of screams from the room above. The Headmaster looked up slightly apprehensively at the electric-light fixture, a marble bowl on chains, which was swaying immediately above his head. "And now, Mr Marshall Calder," he said, "before you make up your mind whether you will step into the breach, I've no doubt that you would like to inspect the school buildings."

The older classrooms at Bogglesham Grammar School were like the older classrooms at any school, only a bit more so. The inky, mutilated desks and the highly polished seats managed even in holiday time to convey the boredom and impatience of the generations of children who had been cramped there. In the sun streaming through a window one could see small clouds of last term's chalk. High on a wall was stuck a piece of inky blotting-paper, the only monument perhaps of some old Boggleshamian, now making good or bad in the great world outside. It was all too drearily familiar; from school to Oxford and from Oxford back to school, the fatal parabola of so many would-be writers.

But then the Headmaster opened a door into a different world. "This would be where you would do most of your teaching," he said. It was a corrugated-iron shed, with an echoing floor and walls of varnished match-boarding. "The library and sixth form room," said the Headmaster, noticing my eye straying round the bookshelves.

"It seems curiously Gothic," I said, "for a building of these materials." It was like the place of worship of one of the smaller nonconformist sects.

"To tell you the truth," he answered, "it's the old chapel. We couldn't afford to pull it down."

At that moment I looked down and placed my hand upon his sleeve. At his feet there was a mound of ordure that could have been produced by no dog smaller than a St Bernard or the Hound of the Baskervilles.

"Uhm!" said the Headmaster. "Uhm."

We surveyed it for a brief period like two surrealists appraising an *objet trouvé*. Then the Headmaster pointed to the pitchpine door at the end of the shed. "If you go through there, Mr Marshall Calder, you will find our new chapel, a truly noble pile, where you will observe a light burning perpetually in memory of the dear old Boggleshamians who died in the War." As he turned and made for his house, "Just gonna get a shovel."

When he joined me at the altar a few minutes later, my mind was made up. "If you think I could possibly replace Mr Crump for six weeks, I should like to take the job, sir," I said. "It's exactly what I've been looking for."

Epilogue

THE SHIP COMES HOME

Chapter Ten

The Ship Comes Home

*

EVEN before I went to Bogglesham, my ties with Steyning and Vickybird had been severed. The Ishmaelite in my father was too strong.

After a year in the Bloomsbury flat he declared that he could not sleep in London. He felt stifled with soot and used breath. So he decided that he would go to London every day from Steyning.

There was what we described as a 'good train' from Victoria to Steyning in the evening. Leaving at six p.m. it did the fifty-five miles to the quaint old-fashioned market town in ninety minutes in fair weather. In foul it might be anything up to an hour late.

But in the morning the only train my father could catch left Steyning at seven and did not arrive until a quarter to ten. So that on a five-day week, with trains running to schedule, my father was spending twenty-one hours and fifteen minutes in railway carriages. It gave him, he said, that much longer to work.

Almost immediately he opened a correspondence with Sir Herbert Walker, the railway satrap whose name was blazoned in every booking-hall beneath the byelaws regulating the despatch by rail of goats, prams and coffins (vacant or occupied), suggesting that now he had bought a first-class season ticket to London the railway should at least lay on a second-rate service. It was only necessary, my father pointed out, to run a special train from Steyning to Shoreham, a distance of a mere six miles, to save him an hour and a quarter's travelling every day.

Sir Herbert answered that six miles was inaccurate, as the train would have to return each day to fetch him the next morning. My father then offered to walk to Bramber, which made a mile shorter journey. But there was nowhere at Bramber to leave the train. Sir Herbert offered to have a census of the season-ticket-holders on the branch line to see whether this limited service could be of any use to them.

The census revealed that my father was the only season-ticket-holder. "So you see," wrote Sir Herbert, "that your proposal is quite uneconomic."

My father replied that the census had been made to see whether it would meet the needs of the season-ticket-holders and it revealed that this little train would satisfy the whole demand. My father was a master of the *argumentum ad hominem*, and at last Sir Herbert wrote frankly saying that the Horsham–Shoreham line was run at a loss and had always been run at a loss, and if my father could suggest any means of making it pay, he would let him have any service he wanted.

It was the opening for which my father had been playing. "The answer to your question is quite simple," he replied. "Close down the stations, dismiss the staff, rip up the railway lines, surface the permanent way with tarmac and let it to my cousin who runs the Southdown Bus Service as a speedway for omnibuses and you will turn your loss into a profit."

Sir Herbert replied, "I have instructed the Traffic Manager to call on you next week." And from then on, my father had his special train. If for any reason he did not intend to go up to town one day, he would phone through and tell the railway to send the train off without him. But normally the train, which for technical reasons started at Steyning, would wait at Bramber until he arrived to catch it. He was the schedule. Once or twice when my father overslept, the stationmaster would venture to ring up and say, "The engine-driver says, if we don't run, we won't catch the connection." And once or twice the connection wasn't caught. But there sat the train, waiting each morning for his arrival. It was the triumph of private enterprise over Private Enterprise.

All the same it was a gruelling service, because if my father did not catch the six o'clock train in the evening, it was nine or ten at night before he got home; and though he swore that he could stand the strain during the week, a certain testiness betrayed to my mother the toll it was taking of his strength. It was she who insisted that we should leave the quaint old-fashioned market town. Maids weren't what they had been before the war, and they objected to getting up at half-past five and sometimes not going to bed till nearly eleven.

So just before I left Oxford our 'permanent' home at Steyning was sold up and the geographical link with Vickybird was broken. I was very sorry to have left that particular part of the South Downs as it was the only part of the earth which I had ever come to know with intimacy. It had taught me what the love of countryside could mean to those who have always had one place which they can consider their own.

But I was not really sorry to see no more of Vickybird. He belonged so intensely to my adolescence that I felt that if I met him in young manhood the vivid impressions he had left on me would be obliterated without others as forceful taking their place. I suspected also that what little I had given him was the limit of my offering; our relation had been one of unofficial teacher and disciple. I feared that as my growth drew me closer to him, and perhaps beyond, tensions would arise which would spoil what had gone before without a mature friendship being developed.

Nevertheless I was intrigued some time after I returned to London, having done my two years hard as a schoolmaster, to receive a letter addressed to me care of my publisher.

> My dear little Arthur,
>
> If it so chance that you live in London town or on occasion visit the Gt. City, please to call this telephone number and remember this address. After its long odyssey, my ship has come in. Praised be the W.O.G.,
>
> > Thine,
> > Vickybird.

I went to the nearest telephone and dialled his number. Someone else answered and I could hear the cavernous bawling upstairs which betokens a furnished apartment. There was a silence and then a voice said "Halloo."

Despite a refinement which I had never noticed, Vickybird's voice was faintly recognisable, as though he was a spirit addressing me through a woman medium from Balham.

"It's Arthur," I said. "I got your letter. Can I come round to see you?"

Immediately his voice changed into one of genuine pleasure and, after a brief conversation, it was fixed that I should go to tea the next day at four o'clock. The 'Halloo' was not the effect of the telephone on Vickybird's voice, but the effect of London. Or was it that until he was certain who was at the other end, he wanted the possibility of retreat?

I associated Vickybird with Steyning, dickering with books in Vine Cottage before going for a walk, whistling imperiously to his heedless bitch, standing suddenly on a stile with his brown locks swaying in the wind, his fag-end sticking to the lower lip, watching a cowman herd his muddy milkers past him through a gate, and declaiming,

> Who are these coming to the sacrifice?
>   To what green altar, O mysterious priest,
> Lead'st thou that heifer lowing at the skies,
>   And all her silken flanks with garlands drest?

I found it hard to visualise him in London; it seemed almost as inappropriate as meeting one's bishop in a bagnio; and yet what I regarded as the normal habitat of Vickybird was to him merely a protracted exile, perhaps the least significant part of his life.

I had in fact once visited London with Vickybird. It was shortly after he had spoken at the Poetry Society. The confidence which he had regained that evening in Oxford led him to make forays to the far more dangerous metropolis on cheap-day tickets. "The time has come," he said, "to pick up old threads." Finding that I was going to London on the same day, he insisted that I should join him in calling on some old threads in St John's Wood.

They lived in the trimmest mews I have ever seen, a mews that had never echoed to the shoes of carriage-horses or the back-fire of a car, but was apparently designed by some visionary architect who foresaw that coachmen's cottages would one day be the houses of the poorer rich. Instead of garages, there was a group of studios. Never having been in a studio, I was enormously excited.

The particular studio we visited belonged to a grizzled painter, who had been gassed, wounded or shell-shocked in the war. He said nothing and most of the time stood as quiet as an animal in the snow listening. But occasionally he silently thrust bread and butter at Vickybird, his wife or me.

His two sons, who had the sensuous beauty of Botticelli's boys, were as quiet as their father, moving delicately about the studio like tame deer, with a gentle pensiveness which was restful.

Their mother, from whom clearly they had derived their beauty, was perhaps the cause of their reticence; she spoke, as it were, for all of them. She was the equal of any American club-woman in her command of language and was all in favour of 'the Progressive Thing.' She spoke of Bernard Shaw and H. G. Wells, Havelock Ellis, Freud, Marx and D. H. Lawrence in the same breath; they all were part of the *Zeitgeist*, weren't they, and interested in the Progressive Thing.

As I listened to this beautiful woman, I thought to myself, "This is the perfection of culture. These authors who for you exemplify violently conflicting views with all of which you agree some of the time, but with none all of the time, have been absorbed and synthesised by this remarkable woman. How *nice* she makes them all!"

The only person who ventured disagreement at times was Vickybird. When he spoke, she immediately deferred. From being the teacher, she became in an instant the disciple, humble, attentive, starry-eyed. I had never seen Vickybird with an audience like this even at the Sanctuary.

Perhaps, I reflected, as I left the studio, that was the reason why Vickybird had insisted that I should watch him pick this old thread up.

The house where Vickybird was staying was in a pleasant, shady street, a lot posher than the place where I was rooming in Hampstead. At the back there was a large and pleasant garden, over which his spacious bed-sitting room looked. He was clean-shaven and his face was for the first time free of scars. He was attired in a lounge-suit, which if not in the height of fashion was the smartest outfit I had ever seen him wear.

"Welcome, little Arthur," he said, wringing me by the hand. "How doth the world use thee? Prithee T.A.P., Take a Pew."

"Let me look at you," I said, taking him by the shoulders. "I've never seen you looking so well. Tell me what's happened. How did the ship come home?"

He made me sit down and sat opposite me. I pulled out

a packet of Player's, took one for myself and offered him one.

"No," he said, "I've given up smoking. I don't need it any more."

"Don't be absurd," I said. "Have one because you enjoy it."

"So be it," he said. "In celebration of this memorable reunion I shall smoke a cigarette." It had always been his way to find the momentous in the trivial, to elevate a half of bitter to an orgy. The cigarette was invested with the gaiety of a forbidden spree. "Many is the time, little Arthur," he said, "when I have said unto thee in the words of the Prophet, 'Cast thy bread upon the waters and it shall come unto thee with knobs on.' That is precisely what has happened. Many moons ago, in the days of my former prosperity, I lent a trifling sum to a colleague of mine in distress. I never thought to press him for repayment and perhaps for that reason he retained for me what is more important than gratitude, an affectionate regard. So it happens that when in the fullness of time my friend becomes the editor of that pre-eminently intellectual organ, the *Sunday Referee*, and it is decided to send its rising circulation soaring still higher by means of a weekly Poetry Competition, who does he select for the key post of Poetry Editor, but yours truly?"

I confess that after the grandiloquent introduction I was expecting something rather more impressive, and I said the first thing which came into my mind. "Well, that at least will pay the rent."

"The emolument," said Vickybird, "if not princely, is more than adequate. But you see, surely, the true significance of this appointment. It gives me, after all these years of waiting, a Platform, a National Platform, from which to spread the Word. It means that at last I can speak to the Youth, in whom our great hope lies. It means . . ."

At this moment the door opened and the beautiful wife of the silent painter walked in with a shopping basket in her hand. She was looking as picturesque and spiritual as ever.

Vickybird tossed the stub of his cigarette behind the gas-stove and then with an appearance of unconcern he said, "Let me see, you both have met, haven't you?" as if he was sure that one of us had met, but uncertain about the other.

"Of course Arthur and I have met," she said; "you brought him to the studio."

"How are your two lovely sons?" I asked.

"Oh, they are very happy, thank you," she answered.

Vickybird had gone over to her and started fussing about unpacking her shopping basket. "Are you quite certain you've got everything?" he asked, "the bread and the cakes? Splendid! Splendid!"

"Of course I've got everything," she said, with a shade of impatience. "What is the matter?"

Vickybird was betraying signs of urgent discomfort, like a small boy who wants to leave the room and is not sure that he can wait for permission. "But you didn't get any cigarettes though, did you?"

"You never asked me to," she answered, "and anyway you've given up smoking."

"But little Arthur smokes," he said.

"I've got plenty," I answered. "Please don't trouble to get any for me."

"When you come to see me," he said with an uncharacteristic grandeur, "you do not smoke your own."

There was a muffled colloquy between the two of them, at the end of which Vickybird took from her the sum of elevenpence halfpenny and skipped from the room.

"I am very glad to hear about Vickybird's job," I said as the door closed.

"It is very gratifying when a Genius is recognised in his own lifetime," she answered. "And we look on it as a victory for the Progressive Thing."

She sat down and indicated that I should sit in a chair opposite. I lit a cigarette and waited for her to speak. It was clear that she wanted to say something, but that despite her command of language she could not for the moment find the precise form of words which would express her mind. The fine mesh of her mind that could strain *Lady Chatterley's Lover* and the case-histories of Havelock Ellis of their 'ostrobogulosity' seemed for the moment clogged by some impurity.

"Has Vicky told you about Us?" she said suddenly. I shook my head. "Well," she said, "we're ... we're Trying the Modern Experiment." It was as if the filter of her mind had suddenly become unstopped. A smile of spiritual relief transfigured her face, as though she had solved a problem which had been worrying her for some time. "Yes, that's what it is."

It was an age in which it was fashionable for young people to go "Lawrencing off together." But Vickybird and the painter's wife were no longer young except in heart. Despite "progressive" views and an Edwardian faith in human perfectibility, they held marriage and family responsibility more highly than many conventional people. Of all the cases of divine possession I have mentioned, theirs was the most certain. Eros, that capricious familiar of the Pantheon, had entered into them both. "The Modern Experiment," a phrase which on first hearing I took to be a euphemism for others which come harsher off the tongue, was really an embarrassed synonym for The Ancient Spell of Human Love.

When, after protracted arguments between love and duty, the former had triumphed, it did not as many fiery passions burn itself to dust. It broke like a fine dawn over the Poet's life.

He had a genius, a rare spirit even, whose frenzy was shot with supernatural hues. I am not in the company of those who think that his genius found expression in his poetry. I think that in that incarnation tragedy struck too hard too young for him to find the unique expression of his visions in verse. They strayed like clouds across his mind, unprecipitated. But he was made from the same stuff as great poets; a Prometheus bound before he could make fire.

Yet finding in his last years a woman who believed in his genius without any of the doubts by which he himself was haunted, he reached a plane of elevated tranquillity which after the middle years of secluded self-torment must have seemed bliss.

Those talks on Blake, to which in the Twenties strolling

with him through the Weald I listened, a fascinated
and bewildered pupil, were expanded in that late London
period into a series of addresses on Poesy in general and
the Prophetic Books in particular, to which the Youth of
the Thirties, including Dylan Thomas, Pamela Hansford
Johnson and Ruthven Todd, listened with the same odd
combination of obscurity and illumination I had felt.